ISSN 0081-4539

2008

THE STATE OF FOOD AND AGRICULTURE

FOOD AND AGRICULTURE ORGANIZATION OF THE UNITED NATIONS
Rome, 2008

Produced by the
Electronic Publishing Policy and Support Branch
Communication Division
FAO

ISBN 978-92-5-105980-7

Contents

BOXES

FIGURES

Foreword

More than at any time in the past three decades, the world's attention is focused this year on food and agriculture. A variety of factors have combined to raise food prices to the highest levels since the 1970s (in real terms), with serious implications for food security among poor populations around the world. One of the most frequently mentioned contributing factors is the rapid recent growth in the use of agricultural commodities – including some food crops – for the production of biofuels. Yet the impact of biofuels on food prices remains the subject of considerable debate, as does their potential to contribute to energy security, climate-change mitigation and agricultural development. Even while this debate continues, countries around the world confront important choices about policies and investments regarding biofuels. These were among the topics discussed at FAO in June 2008 by delegations from 181 countries attending the High-Level Conference on World Food Security: the Challenges of Climate Change and Bioenergy. Given the urgency of these choices and the magnitude of their potential consequences, participants at the Conference agreed that careful assessment of the prospects, risks and opportunities posed by biofuels is essential. This is the focus of FAO's 2008 report on the *State of Food and Agriculture*.

The report finds that while biofuels will offset only a modest share of fossil energy use over the next decade, they will have much bigger impacts on agriculture and food security. The emergence of biofuels as a new and significant source of demand for some agricultural commodities – including maize, sugar, oilseeds and palm oil – contributes to higher prices for agricultural commodities in general, and for the resources used to produce them. For the majority of poor households who consume more food than they produce, higher prices can pose a serious threat to food security – especially in the short term. But it is important to keep in mind that biofuels are only one of many drivers of high food prices: weather-related production shortfalls in major exporting countries, low global cereal stocks, increasing fuel costs, the changing structure of demand associated with income growth, population growth and urbanization, operations on financial markets, short-term policy actions, exchange rate fluctuations and other factors also play a role. Given appropriate policies and investments, high prices can trigger a response in terms of increased agricultural production and employment, which could contribute to poverty alleviation and improved food security over the longer term.

The report also finds that the impact of biofuels on greenhouse gas emissions varies widely, depending on where and how the various feedstock crops are produced. In many cases, increased emissions from land-use change are likely to offset or even exceed the greenhouse gas savings obtained by replacing fossil fuels with biofuels, and impacts on water, soil and biodiversity are also a concern. Good agricultural practices and increased yields through technological developments and improved infrastructure can help reduce some of these adverse impacts. In the longer run, the emergence of second-generation biofuels may offer additional benefits.

These are some of the main conclusions. What are their implications for policy? Our starting point must be the current situation of soaring food prices and the severe problems they pose for the poor. There is an urgent need to provide immediate relief and assistance to the net food-importing developing countries most affected by higher food prices, as well as providing safety nets to poor net food-buying households in developing countries. This is a shared responsibility of national governments and the international community. However, it is advisable to avoid policies such as export bans and direct price controls, which may in fact worsen and prolong the crisis by blocking price incentives for farmers and preventing them from increasing output.

There is also an urgent need to review current policies supporting, subsidising and mandating biofuel production and use. A large share of the recent growth in biofuels has been driven by such policies, especially in Organisation for Economic Co-operation and Development (OECD) countries. Many of the assumptions underlying these policies regarding beneficial impacts on climate change and energy security are now being questioned, and unintended consequences of rising food prices for poor consumers are being recognized. There seems to be a case for directing expenditures on biofuels more towards research and development, especially on second-generation technologies, which hold more promise in terms of reductions in greenhouse gas emissions with less pressure on the natural resource base.

Effective action must be undertaken to ensure that biofuels provide a positive contribution to reductions in greenhouse gas emissions while minimizing other negative environmental impacts. There is a need, especially, for a much better understanding of the effects of biofuels on land-use change, from which the most significant impacts on greenhouse gas emissions and other environmental impacts will be derived. Criteria for sustainable production of biofuels can help ensure environmental sustainability. However, it is critical that such criteria be carefully assessed and applied only to global public goods, and they must be designed in such a way as to avoid the creation of additional trade barriers and posing undue constraints on developing countries wishing to take advantage of the opportunities offered by biofuels.

When we look to the longer run, to the extent demand for biofuels leads to a continued upward pressure on prices for agricultural commodities, we must be able to reap the opportunities this provides for agricultural development and poverty alleviation. This requires overcoming some of the long-run constraints which have hampered agricultural development in too many developing countries for too long. The emergence of biofuels as a new source of demand for agricultural commodities strengthens the case for enhanced investments, as well as increased levels of development assistance, directed towards the agriculture sector and the

rural areas. Particular attention needs to be given to ensuring that farmers have access to necessary inputs such as irrigation, fertilizers and improved seed varieties through market-supportive mechanisms. Opportunities for developing countries to take advantage of biofuel demand would also be greatly advanced by the removal of the agricultural and biofuel subsidies and trade barriers that currently benefit producers in OECD countries at the expense of producers in developing countries.

The future of biofuels and the role they will play for agriculture and food security remain uncertain. There are many concerns and challenges to be overcome if biofuels are to contribute positively to an improved environment as well as to agricultural and rural development. But just as hasty decisions to promote biofuels may have adverse unintended consequences on food security and the environment, so might hasty decisions to restrict biofuels limit opportunities for sustainable agricultural growth that could benefit the poor. As noted in the Declaration adopted at the June 2008 High-Level Conference on World Food Security, "It is essential to address the challenges and opportunities posed by biofuels, in view of the world's food security, energy and sustainable development needs. We are convinced that in-depth studies are necessary to ensure that production and use of biofuels is sustainable in accordance with the three pillars of sustainable development and take into account the need to achieve and maintain global food security … We call upon relevant inter-governmental organizations, including FAO, within their mandates and areas of expertise, with the involvement of national governments, partnerships, the private sector, and civil society, to foster a coherent, effective and results-oriented international dialogue on biofuels in the context of food security and sustainable development needs." It is my hope that this report will contribute to better-informed dialogue and policy action in this area of critical choices we face.

Jacques Diouf
FAO DIRECTOR-GENERAL

Acknowledgements

The State of Food and Agriculture 2008 was written by a core team led by Keith Wiebe and comprising André Croppenstedt, Terri Raney, Jakob Skoet and Monika Zurek, all of the FAO Agricultural and Development Economics Division of FAO; Jeff Tschirley, Chair of the FAO Inter-Departmental Working Group on Bioenergy; and Merritt Cluff of the FAO Trade and Markets Division. The report was co-edited by Terri Raney, Jakob Skoet and Jeff Tschirley. Bernardete Neves provided research assistance and Liliana Maldonado and Paola di Santo provided secretarial and administrative support.

In addition to the core team, several people prepared background papers and analysis or drafted sections of the report: Astrid Agostini, El Mamoun Amrouk, Jacob Burke, Concepción Calpe, Patricia Carmona Ridondo, Roberto Cuevas García, David Dawe, Olivier Dubois, Jippe Hoogeveen, Lea Jenin, Charlotta Jull, Yianna Lambrou, Irini Maltsoglou, Holger Matthey, Jamie Morgan, Victor Mosoti, Adam Prakash, Andrea Rossi, John Ruane, Gregoire Tallard, James Tefft, Peter Thoenes and Miguel Trossero, all of FAO; Uwe Fritsche, Oeko-Institute; Bernd Franke, Guido Reinhardt and Julia Münch, IFEU Institute; Martin von Lampe, OECD; Ronald Steenblik, Global Subsidies Initiative, IISD; and Wyatt Thompson, Food and Agriculture Policy Research Institute. The report also drew on the joint OECD-FAO *Agricultural Outlook 2008–2017* and policy scenarios that were prepared by the FAO Trade and Markets Division on the basis of the AgLink-Cosimo model and discussions with the OECD Secretariat. These contributions are gratefully acknowledged.

The report was prepared under the overall guidance of Hafez Ghanem, Assistant Director-General of FAO's Economic and Social Development Department. Valuable advice was received from the members of the report's External Advisory Board: Walter Falcon (chair), Stanford University; Kym Anderson, University of Adelaide; Simeon Ehui, World Bank; Franz Heidhues, University of Hohenheim; and Eugenia Muchnik, Fundación Chile.

The team benefited greatly from a wide range of consultations on biofuels, including: two Technical Consultations on Bioenergy and Food Security, held in Rome, 16–18 April 2007 and 5–6 February 2008, under the auspices of the German-funded Bioenergy and Food Security (BEFS) Project; the International Workshop on Economics, Policies and Science of Bioenergy, jointly sponsored by FAO and the International Consortium on Agricultural Biotechnology Research in Ravello, Italy, 26 July 2007; and two expert consultations on Bioenergy Policy, Markets and Trade and Food Security and Global Perspectives on Fuel and Food Security in Rome, 18–20 February 2008. Several meetings of the FAO Inter-Departmental Working Group on Bioenergy reviewed drafts of the report, and it was presented to the Economic and Social Development Department management team on 26 March 2008, all FAO staff members on 31 March 2008 and the FAO senior management team on 26 May 2008.

Many people gave valuable advice, suggestions and review comments on the report, individually or in the context of the above-mentioned consultations: Abdolreza Abbassian, Gustavo Anríquez, Boubaker Benbelhassen, Jim Carle, Romina Cavatassi, Albertine Delange, Olivier Dubois, Aziz Elbehri, Barbara Ekwall, Erika Felix, Margarita Flores, Theodor Friedrich, Daniel Gustafson, Maarten Immink, Kaori Izumi, Brahim Kebe, Modeste Kinane, Rainer Krell, Eric Kueneman, Preetmoninder Lidder, Pascal Liu, Attaher Maiga, Michela Morese, Alexander Müller, Jennifer Nyberg, David Palmer, Shivaji Pandey, Wim Polman, Adam Prakash, Andrea Rossi, John Ruane, Mirella Salvatore, Alexander Sarris, Josef Schmidhuber, Annika Söder, Andrea Sonnino, Pasquale Steduto, Diana Templeman, Nuria Urquía, Jessica Vapnek, Margret Vidar, Andreas Von Brandt, Adrian Whiteman and Alberto Zezza, all of FAO; and Ricardo Abramovay, University of

São Paulo; Dale Andrew, OECD; Melvyn Askew, Harper Adams University College; Mary Bohman, Cheryl Christiansen, Steve Crutchfield and Carol Jones, USDA Economic Research Service; David Cooper and Markus Lehman, Convention on Biological Diversity; Martin Banse, Agricultural Economics Research Institute (LEI); Eduardo Calvo, IPPC WG III; Harry de Gorter, Cornell University; Hartwig de Haen; Daniel de la Torre Ugarte, University of Tennessee; Ewout Deurwaarder and Paul Hodson, Energy and Transport Directorate-General of the European Commission; Asbjørn Eide, Norwegian Centre for Human Rights; Francis Epplin, Oklahoma State University; Polly Ericksen, Oxford University; Andre Faaij, Utrecht University; Günter Fischer, International Institute for Applied Systems Analysis (IAASA); Richard Flavell, Ceres, Inc.; Julie Flood, CABI; Thomas Funke, University of Pretoria; Janet Hall, UN Foundation; Neeta Hooda, UNFCCC; Barbara Huddleston, Stockholm Environment Institute; Tatsuiji Koizumi, MAFF, Japan; Samai Jai-in, Thailand National Metal and Materials Technology Centre; Francis Johnson, Stockholm Environment Institute; David Lee, Cornell University; Bruce McCarl, Texas A&M University; Enrique Manzanilla, US Environmental Protection Agency; Teresa Malyshev, International Energy Agency; Ferdinand Meyer, University of Pretoria; Willi Meyers, University of Missouri; José Roberto Moreira, University of São Paulo; Siwa Msangi and Gerald Nelson, IFPRI; Martina Otto, UNEP; Joe Outlaw, Texas A&M University; Jyoti Parikh, Integrated Research and Action for Development (India); Prabhu Pingali, Bill and Melinda Gates Foundation; Martin Rice, Earth System Science Partnership; C. Ford Runge, University of Minnesota; Roger Sedjo, Resources for the Future; Seth Shames, Ecoagriculture Partners; Guy Sneyers, Common Fund for Commodities; Steve Wiggins, ODI; Erik Wijkstrom, WTO; Simonetta Zarrilli, UNCTAD; and David Zilberman, University of California-Berkeley.

The expert contributions of the editors, translators, designers, layout artists and reproduction specialists of the FAO Knowledge and Communication Department are gratefully acknowledged.

Abbreviations and acronyms

EU   European Union

CRB   Commodity Research Bureau

GBEP   Global Bioenergy Partnership

GDP   gross domestic product

IRR   internal rate of return

LDC   least-developed country

LIFDC   low-income food-deficit country

MFN   most-favoured nation

Mtoe   million tonnes of oil equivalent

NPV   net present value

OECD   Organisation for Economic Co-operation and Development

TSE   total support estimates

WTO   World Trade Organization

Part I

BIOFUELS:
PROSPECTS, RISKS
AND OPPORTUNITIES

Part I

1. Introduction and key messages

When the initial preparations for the 2008 issue of *The State of Food and Agriculture* began, two years ago, there were high expectations surrounding liquid biofuels as a resource that could potentially mitigate global climate change, contribute to energy security and support agricultural producers around the world. Many governments cited these goals as justification for implementing policies promoting the production and use of liquid biofuels based on agricultural commodities.

Since then, there has been a marked change in perceptions of biofuels. Recent analysis has raised serious questions regarding the full environmental impacts of producing biofuels from an already stressed agricultural resource base. The costs of policies aimed at promoting liquid biofuels – and their possible unintended consequences – are beginning to attract scrutiny. Food prices have risen rapidly, sparking protests in many countries and giving rise to major concerns over the food security of the world's most vulnerable people.

However, biofuels are only one of many factors that have driven the recent rise in commodity prices. Also, biofuels have other implications beyond their effect on commodity prices. This issue of *The State of Food and Agriculture* surveys the current state of the debate on biofuels and explores these implications. It examines the policies being implemented in support of biofuels and the policies that would be needed to address their implications for the environment, food security and the poor.

Agriculture and energy

Agriculture and energy have always been tied by close links, but the nature and strength of the relationship have changed over time. Agriculture has always been a source of energy, and energy is a major input in modern agricultural production. Until the nineteenth century, animals provided almost all the "horse power" used for transport and farm equipment, and in many parts of the world they still do. Agriculture produces the "fuel" to feed these animals; two centuries ago, around 20 percent of the agricultural area in the United States of America was used to feed draught animals (Sexton *et al.*, 2007).

The linkages between agriculture and energy output markets weakened in the twentieth century as fossil fuels gained prominence in the transport sector. At the same time, linkages on the input side strengthened as agriculture became increasingly reliant on chemical fertilizers derived from fossil fuels and machinery powered by diesel. Food storage, processing and distribution, too, are often energy-intensive activities. Higher energy costs, therefore, have a direct and strong impact on agricultural production costs and food prices.

The recent emergence of liquid biofuels based on agricultural crops as transport fuels has reasserted the linkages between energy and agricultural output markets. Liquid biofuels have the potential to exert a significant effect on agricultural markets, but they are, and are likely to remain, a

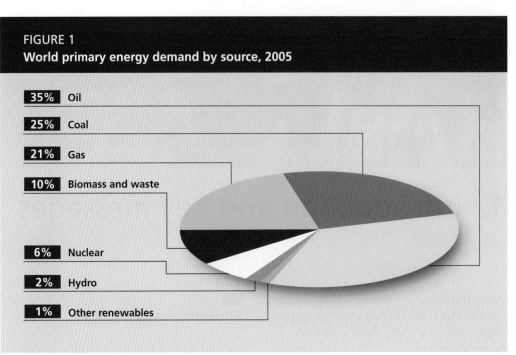

FIGURE 1
World primary energy demand by source, 2005

35% Oil
25% Coal
21% Gas
10% Biomass and waste
6% Nuclear
2% Hydro
1% Other renewables

Source: IEA, 2007.

relatively small part of the overall energy market. The world's total primary energy demand amounts to about 11 400 million tonnes of oil equivalent (Mtoe) per year (IEA, 2007); biomass, including agricultural and forest products and organic wastes and residues, accounts for 10 percent of this total (Figure 1). Fossil fuels are by far the dominant source of primary energy in the world, with oil, coal and gas together supplying more than 80 percent of the total.

Renewable energy sources represent around 13 percent of total primary energy supply, with biomass dominating the renewable sector. The sources of primary energy differ markedly across regions (Figure 2). In some developing countries, as much as 90 percent of the total energy consumption is supplied by biomass. Solid biofuels such as fuelwood, charcoal and animal dung constitute by far the largest segment of the bioenergy sector, representing a full 99 percent of all biofuels. For millennia, humans have depended on the use of biomass for heating and cooking, and developing countries in Africa and Asia remain heavily dependent on these traditional uses of biomass. Liquid biofuels play a much more limited role in global energy supply and account for only 1.9 percent of total bioenergy. Their significance lies mainly in the transport

sector, but even here they supplied only 0.9 percent of total transport fuel consumption in 2005, up from 0.4 percent in 1990.

In recent years, however, liquid biofuels have grown rapidly in terms of volume and of share of global demand for transport energy. The growth is projected to continue, as illustrated by Figure 3, which shows historical trends as well as projections to 2015 and 2030, as reported in the *World Energy Outlook 2007* (IEA, 2007).[1] Nevertheless, the contribution of liquid biofuels to transport energy and, even more so, to global energy use, will remain limited. Global primary energy demand is, and will remain, overwhelmingly dominated by fossil fuels – with coal, oil and gas currently accounting for 81 percent of the total. This share is forecast at 82 percent in 2030, with coal increasing its share at the expense of oil. Biomass and waste products currently cover 10 percent of global primary energy demand, a share that is forecast to decline slightly to 9 percent by 2030. By the same year, liquid

---

[1] The projection refers to the IEA's so-called "Reference Scenario", which "is designed to show the outcome, on given assumptions about economic growth, population, energy prices and technology, if nothing more is done by governments to change underlying energy trends". The projections and underlying assumptions are discussed in Chapter 4.

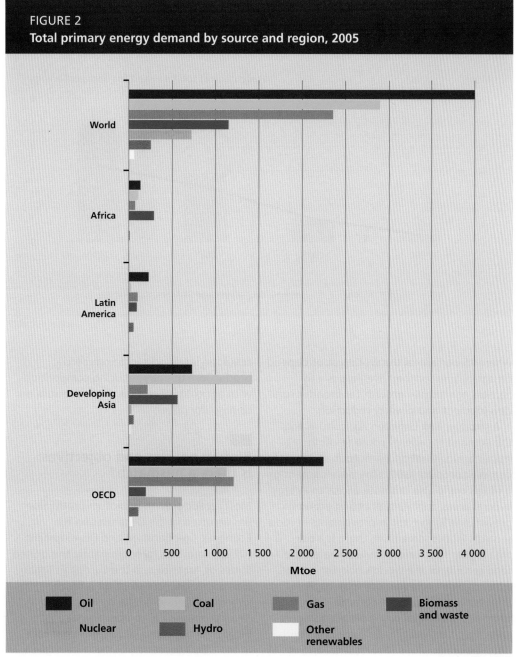

FIGURE 2
Total primary energy demand by source and region, 2005

Source: IEA, 2007.

biofuels are projected to represent the still modest share of 3.0–3.5 percent of global transport energy consumption.

Opportunities and risks for liquid biofuels

Notwithstanding the limited importance of liquid biofuels in terms of global energy supply, also compared with that of solid biofuels, their direct and significant effects on global agricultural markets, on the environment and on food security are already generating debate and controversy. This new source of demand for agricultural commodities creates opportunities, but also risks, for the food and agriculture sectors. Indeed, the demand for biofuels could reverse the declining trend in real commodity prices that has depressed agricultural growth in much of the developing world over recent decades. As such, biofuels may offer an opportunity for developing countries –

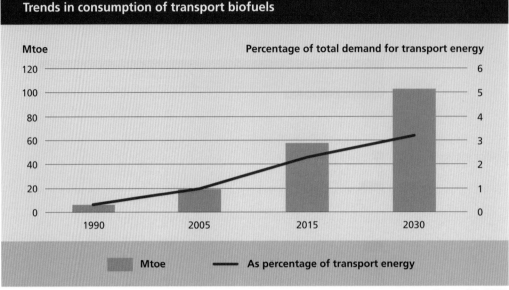

FIGURE 3
Trends in consumption of transport biofuels

Source: IEA, 2007.

where 75 percent of the world's poor depend on agriculture for their livelihoods – to harness agricultural growth for broader rural development and poverty reduction.

A stronger link between agriculture and the demand for energy could result in higher agricultural prices, output and gross domestic product (GDP). The development of biofuels could also promote access to energy in rural areas, further supporting economic growth and long-term improvements in food security. At the same time, there is a risk that higher food prices could threaten the food security of the world's poorest people, many of whom spend more than half of their household incomes on food. Moreover, demand for biofuels could place additional pressure on the natural resource base, with potentially harmful environmental and social consequences, particularly for people who already lack access to energy, food, land and water.

Given current agronomic and conversion technologies, the economic viability of most liquid biofuels in many, but not all, countries is tenuous without support and subsidies. However, improved crop yields, area expansion and intensification could expand feedstock production significantly and reduce costs. Technological innovation in biofuel processing could also lower costs dramatically, potentially bringing second-generation biofuels derived from

cellulosic feedstocks into commercial production, thereby reducing competition with agricultural crops and the pressure on commodity prices.

Biofuel policies and objectives: is there a mismatch?

Most recent growth in biofuel production has occurred in the Organisation for Economic Co-operation and Development (OECD) countries, predominantly the United States of America and the European Union (EU) countries. An exception is Brazil, which has pioneered the development of an economically competitive national biofuel sector based largely on sugar cane. In the OECD countries, biofuels have been promoted by policies supporting and subsidizing production and consumption; such policies are now being introduced in a number of developing countries.

The main drivers behind OECD country policies have been the objectives of energy security and climate-change mitigation through reduced greenhouse gas emissions combined with a desire to support agriculture and promote rural development. These concerns are not diminishing; indeed, climate change and future energy security continue to move higher up the international policy agenda. However, the role of biofuels in addressing these concerns, including the appropriate policies to be applied, is now coming under closer scrutiny. Questions are being asked about the coherence of current policies and some of the underlying assumptions, and new concerns are coming to the forefront.

First of all, the policies being pursued are costly. Indeed, estimates of prevailing biofuel subsidies are high considering the still relatively limited role of biofuels in world energy supply. Estimates by the Global Subsidies Initiative for the EU, the United States of America and three other OECD countries (see Chapter 3) suggest a total level of support to biodiesel and ethanol in 2006 of around US$11–12 billion (Steenblik, 2007). On a per-litre basis, support ranges between US$0.20 and US$1.00. With increasing levels of biofuel production and support, costs could escalate. While it can be claimed that subsidies are only intended to be temporary, whether this will be the case will obviously hinge on the long-term economic viability of biofuels. This, in turn, will depend on the cost of other energy sources, whether they be fossil fuels or, in the longer term, alternative sources of renewable energy. Even taking into account recent rises in oil prices, among the major producers only Brazilian sugar-cane ethanol currently appears to be competitive with fossil fuel counterparts without subsidies.

Direct subsidies, however, represent only the most obvious cost; other hidden costs are the outcome of distorted resource allocation resulting from selective support to biofuels and quantitative tools such as blending mandates. For decades, agricultural subsidies and protectionism in numerous OECD countries have led to major misallocation of resources at the international level, with heavy costs both to consumers in the OECD countries and to developing countries. Such misallocation risks being perpetuated and exacerbated by current biofuel policies in OECD countries.

Another cost dimension, in addition to the total cost consideration, is linked to the effectiveness in reaching stated objectives. Biofuel policies are often justified on the basis of multiple, sometimes competing, objectives, and this lack of clarity can lead to policies that fail to achieve their objectives or do so only at very high costs. An example

is the high cost of reducing greenhouse gas emissions through substitution of fossil energy with biofuels (Doornbosch and Steenblik, 2007). The cost-effectiveness of achieving emission reductions through biofuel development is increasingly questioned, especially if biofuel development is not integrated into a wider framework encompassing energy conservation, transport policies and the development of other forms of renewable energy.

Similarly, the technical efficiency of biofuels in contributing to reduced emissions is also coming under scrutiny, depending on the type of biofuel and its origin in terms of crop and location. Taking into account the complete production process for biofuels and possible land-use changes needed to expand feedstock production may critically alter the presumed favourable greenhouse gas balance sheet for biofuels. Indeed, recent research suggests that large-scale expansion of biofuel production could lead to net increases in greenhouse gas emissions.

Other environmental sustainability issues are also coming to the forefront. Although bioenergy can provide environmental gains, its production also has the potential to cause environmental damage. The impact of expanded biofuel production on land and water resources and on biodiversity is the focus of increasing attention, as is the question of how to ensure its environmental sustainability.

Biofuel policies have generally been designed within a national framework with little regard for unintended consequences at the national and international levels. As the implications of biofuel development for developing countries are scrutinized more closely, one emerging concern is the negative impact of high food prices – which are partly a result of increased competition from biofuels for agricultural output and resources – on poverty and food security.

At the same time, increasing demand for biofuels may offer opportunities for farmers and rural communities in developing countries and thus contribute to rural development. However, their capacity to take advantage of these opportunities depends on the existence of an enabling environment. At the global level, current trade policies – characterized by high degrees of support and protection – do not favour developing country participation or an efficient international pattern of biofuel production. At the domestic level, farmers depend critically on the existence of an appropriate policy framework and the necessary physical and institutional infrastructure.

The report looks more closely at these issues in the light of the most recent emerging evidence.

Key messages of the report

- **Demand for agricultural feedstocks for liquid biofuels will be a significant factor for agricultural markets and for world agriculture over the next decade and perhaps beyond.** The demand for biofuel feedstocks may help reverse the long-term decline in real agricultural commodity prices, creating both opportunities and risks. All countries will face the impacts of liquid biofuel development – whether or not they participate directly in the sector – because all agricultural markets will be affected.

- **Rapidly growing demand for biofuel feedstocks has contributed to higher food prices, which pose an immediate threat to the food security of poor net food buyers (in value terms) in both urban and rural areas.** Many of the world's poor spend more than half of their household incomes on food, and even in rural areas the majority of the poor are net purchasers of food. Safety nets are urgently needed to protect the world's poorest and most vulnerable people and to ensure their access to adequate food. But safety nets should be carefully targeted and should not block the transmission of price signals to agricultural producers.

- **In the longer term, expanded demand and increased prices for agricultural commodities may represent opportunities for agricultural and rural development.** However, market opportunities cannot overcome existing social and institutional barriers to equitable growth – with exclusion factors such as gender, ethnicity and political powerlessness – and may even worsen them. Moreover, higher commodity prices alone are not

enough; investments in productivity and sustainability-enhancing research, enabling institutions, infrastructure and sound policies are also urgently needed. A strong focus on the needs of the poorest and least resource-endowed population groups is crucial to ensure broad-based rural development.

- **The impact of biofuels on greenhouse gas emissions – one of the key motivations underlying support to the biofuel sector – differs according to feedstock, location, agricultural practice and conversion technology.** In many cases, the net effect is unfavourable. The largest impact is determined by land-use change – for example through deforestation – as agricultural area is expanded to meet growing demand for biofuel feedstocks. Several other possible negative environmental effects – on land and water resources, as well as on biodiversity – occur largely because of changes in land use. Accelerated biofuel production, pushed by policy support, strongly enhances the risk of large-scale land-use change and the associated environmental threats.

- **Harmonized approaches for assessing greenhouse gas balances and other environmental impacts of biofuel production are needed to achieve desirable outcomes.** Criteria for sustainable production can contribute to improving the environmental footprint of biofuels, but they must focus on global public goods and be based on internationally agreed standards and must not put developing countries at a competitive disadvantage. The same agricultural commodities should not be treated differently according to whether they are destined for biofuel production or for traditional uses such as human consumption or feed.

- **Liquid biofuels are likely to replace only a small share of global energy supplies and cannot alone eliminate our dependence on fossil fuels.** Land requirements for feedstock production would be too extensive to allow displacement of fossil fuels on a larger scale. The introduction of second-generation biofuels based on lignocellulosic feedstocks could greatly expand potential, but for the foreseeable future liquid biofuels would still be able to supply only a small portion of global transport energy and an even smaller portion of total global energy.

- **Production of liquid biofuels in many countries is not currently economically viable without subsidies, given existing agricultural production and biofuel-processing technologies and recent relative prices of commodity feedstocks and crude oil.** The most significant exception is sugar-cane-based ethanol production in Brazil. Competitiveness varies widely according to the specific biofuel, feedstock and production location, and economic viability can change as countries face changing market prices for inputs and oil, as well as through technological advances in the industry itself. Technological innovation can lower the costs of agricultural production and biofuel processing. Investment in research and development is critical for the future of biofuels as an economically and environmentally sustainable source of renewable energy. This applies both to the field of agronomy and to conversion technologies. Research and development on second-generation technologies, in particular, could significantly enhance the future role of biofuels.

- **Policy interventions, especially in the form of subsidies and mandated blending of biofuels with fossil fuels, are driving the rush to liquid biofuels.** However, many of the measures being implemented by both developed and developing countries have high economic, social and environmental costs. The interactions among agricultural, biofuel and trade policies often discriminate against developing-country producers of biofuel feedstocks and compound impediments to the emergence of biofuel processing and exporting sectors in developing countries. There is a need to review current biofuel policies and carefully assess their costs and consequences.

- **Ensuring environmentally, economically and socially sustainable biofuel production requires policy action in the following broad areas:**
  - protecting the poor and food-insecure;
  - taking advantage of opportunities for agricultural and rural development;
  - ensuring environmental sustainability;
  - reviewing existing biofuel policies;
  - making the international system supportive of sustainable biofuel development.

2. Biofuels and agriculture – a technical overview

Traditional biomass, including fuelwood, charcoal and animal dung, continues to provide important sources of energy in many parts of the world. Bioenergy is the dominant energy source for most of the world's population who live in extreme poverty and who use this energy mainly for cooking. More advanced and efficient conversion technologies now allow the extraction of biofuels – in solid, liquid and gaseous forms – from materials such as wood, crops and waste material. This chapter provides an overview of biofuels. What are they, what is their potential and what are their implications for agriculture? The main focus, however, is on liquid biofuels for transport, which are now gaining in prominence as a result of the rapid increase in their use.

Types of biofuels

Biofuels are energy carriers that store the energy derived from biomass.[2] A wide range of biomass sources can be used to produce bioenergy in a variety of forms. For example, food, fibre and wood process residues from the industrial sector; energy crops, short-rotation crops and agricultural wastes from the agriculture sector; and residues from the forestry sector can all be used to generate electricity, heat, combined heat and power, and other forms of bioenergy. Biofuels may be referred to as *renewable* energy because they are a form of transformed solar energy.

Biofuels can be classified according to source and type. They may be derived from forest, agricultural or fishery products or municipal wastes, as well as from agro-industry, food industry and food service by-products and wastes. They may be *solid*, such as fuelwood, charcoal and wood pellets; *liquid*, such as ethanol, biodiesel and pyrolysis oils; or *gaseous*, such as biogas.

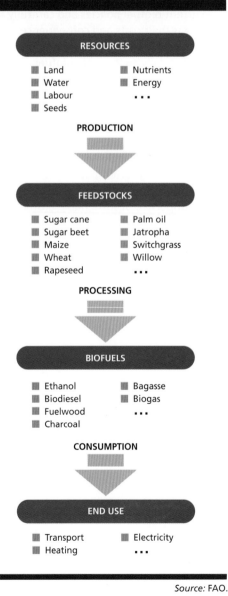

FIGURE 4
Biofuels – from feedstock to end use

RESOURCES

Land	Nutrients
Water	Energy
Labour	...
Seeds	

PRODUCTION

FEEDSTOCKS

Sugar cane	Palm oil
Sugar beet	Jatropha
Maize	Switchgrass
Wheat	Willow
Rapeseed	...

PROCESSING

BIOFUELS

Ethanol	Bagasse
Biodiesel	Biogas
Fuelwood	...
Charcoal	

CONSUMPTION

END USE

Transport	Electricity
Heating	...

Source: FAO.

---

[2] For a review of terminology relating to biofuels, see FAO (2004a).

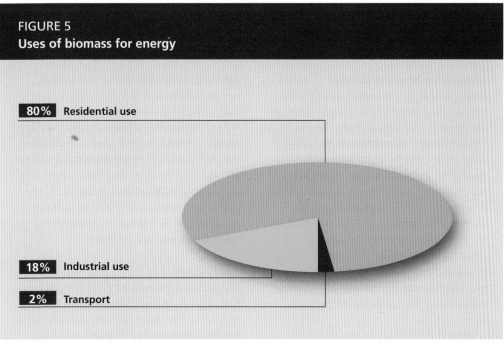

FIGURE 5
Uses of biomass for energy

80% Residential use

18% Industrial use

2% Transport

Source: IEA, 2007.

A basic distinction is also made between *primary* (unprocessed) and *secondary* (processed) biofuels:

- **Primary biofuels**, such as firewood, wood chips and pellets, are those where the organic material is used essentially in its natural form (as harvested). Such fuels are directly combusted, usually to supply cooking fuel, heating or electricity production needs in small- and large-scale industrial applications.

- **Secondary biofuels** in the form of solids (e.g. charcoal), liquids (e.g. ethanol, biodiesel and bio-oil), or gases (e.g. biogas, synthesis gas and hydrogen) can be used for a wider range of applications, including transport and high-temperature industrial processes.

Liquid biofuels for transport[3]

In spite of their limited overall volume (see Figure 5), the strongest growth in recent years has been in liquid biofuels for transport, mostly produced using agricultural and food commodities as feedstocks. The most significant are ethanol and biodiesel.

Ethanol

Any feedstock containing significant amounts of sugar, or materials that can be converted into sugar such as starch or cellulose, can be used to produce ethanol. Ethanol available in the biofuel market today is based on either sugar or starch. Common sugar crops used as feedstocks are sugar cane, sugar beet and, to a lesser extent, sweet sorghum. Common starchy feedstocks include maize, wheat and cassava. The use of biomass containing sugars that can be fermented directly to ethanol is the simplest way of producing ethanol. In Brazil and other tropical countries currently producing ethanol, sugar cane is the most widely used feedstock. In OECD countries, most ethanol is produced from the starchy component of cereals (although sugar beet is also used), which can be converted fairly easily into sugar. However, these starchy products represent only a small percentage of the total plant mass. Most plant matter is composed of cellulose, hemicellulose and lignin; the first two can be converted into alcohol after they have first been converted into sugar, but the process is more difficult than the one for starch. Today, there is virtually no commercial production of ethanol from cellulosic biomass, but substantial research continues in this area (see the section on second-generation biofuels on pp. 18–19).

---

[3] This section is based on GBEP (2007, pp. 2–10) and IEA (2004).

BOX 1
Other types of biomass for heat, power and transport

Biomass for heat and power

A range of biomass resources are used to generate electricity and heat through combustion. Sources include various forms of waste, such as residues from agro-industries, post-harvest residues left on the fields, animal manure, wood wastes from forestry and industry, residues from food and paper industries, municipal solid wastes, sewage sludge and biogas from the digestion of agricultural and other organic wastes. Dedicated energy crops, such as short-rotation perennials (eucalyptus, poplar, willow) and grasses (miscanthus and switchgrass), are also used.

Several processes can be used for power generation. Most biomass-derived electricity is produced using a steam-cycle process: biomass is burned in a boiler to generate high-pressure steam that flows over a series of aerodynamic blades causing a turbine to rotate, which in response turns a connected electric generator to produce electricity. Compacted forms of biomass such as wood pellets and briquettes can also be used for combustion, and biomass can also be burned with coal in the boiler of a conventional power plant to yield steam and electricity. The latter is currently the most cost-efficient method for incorporating renewable technology into conventional power production because much of the existing power plant infrastructure can be used without major modifications.

Biogas for heat, power and transport
Anaerobic digestion

Biogas can be created through the *anaerobic digestion* of food or animal waste by bacteria in an oxygen-starved environment. The resulting biogas contains a high volume of methane along with carbon dioxide, which can be used for heating or for electricity generation in a modified internal combustion engine. The conversion of animal wastes and manure to methane/biogas can bring significant environmental and health benefits. Methane is a greenhouse gas that has a global-warming potential that is 22–24 times more powerful than that of carbon dioxide. By trapping and utilizing the methane, its greenhouse gas impacts are avoided. In addition, heat generated during the biodigestion process kills the pathogens present in manure, and the material left at the end of the process provides a valuable fertilizer.

Gasification

Through the process of *gasification*, solid biomass can be converted into a fuel gas or biogas. Biomass gasifiers operate by heating biomass in a low-oxygen, high-temperature environment that breaks it down to release a flammable, energy-rich synthesis gas or "syngas". This gas can be burned in a conventional boiler, or used instead of natural gas in a gas turbine to turn electric generators. Biogas formed through gasification can be filtered to remove unwanted chemical compounds and can be used in efficient "combined-cycle" power-generation systems that combine steam and gas turbines to generate electricity.

Biogas for transport

Untreated biogas is unsuitable as a transport fuel owing to its low methane content (60–70 percent) and high concentration of contaminants. However, it can be treated to remove carbon dioxide, water and corrosive hydrogen sulphide and to enhance its methane content (to over 95 percent). When compressed, treated biogas has properties similar to those of compressed natural gas, making it suitable for use in transport.

Source: based on GBEP, 2007.

Ethanol can be blended with petrol or burned in its pure form in slightly modified spark-ignition engines. A litre of ethanol contains approximately 66 percent of the energy provided by a litre of petrol, but has a higher octane level and when mixed with petrol for transportation it improves the performance of the latter. It also improves fuel combustion in vehicles, thereby reducing the emission of carbon monoxide, unburned hydrocarbons and carcinogens. However, the combustion of ethanol also causes a heightened reaction with nitrogen in the atmosphere, which can result in a marginal increase in nitrogen oxide gases. In comparison with petrol, ethanol contains only a trace amount of sulphur. Mixing ethanol with petrol, therefore, helps to reduce the fuel's sulphur content and thereby lowers the emissions of sulphur oxide, a component of acid rain and a carcinogen.

Biodiesel

Biodiesel is produced by combining vegetable oil or animal fat with an alcohol and a catalyst through a chemical process known as *transesterification*. Oil for biodiesel production can be extracted from almost any oilseed crop; globally, the most popular sources are rapeseed in Europe and soybean in Brazil and the United States of America. In tropical and subtropical countries, biodiesel is produced from palm, coconut and jatropha oils. Small amounts of animal fat, from fish- and animal-processing operations, are also used for biodiesel production. The production process typically yields additional by-products such as crushed bean "cake" (an animal feed) and glycerine. Because biodiesel can be based on a wide range of oils, the resulting fuels can display a greater variety of physical properties, such as viscosity and combustibility, than ethanol.

Biodiesel can be blended with traditional diesel fuel or burned in its pure form in compression ignition engines. Its energy content is 88–95 percent of that of diesel, but it improves the lubricity of diesel and raises the cetane value, making the fuel economy of both generally comparable. The higher oxygen content of biodiesel aids in the completion of fuel combustion, reducing emissions of particulate air pollutants, carbon monoxide and hydrocarbons.

As with ethanol, diesel also contains only a negligible amount of sulphur, thus reducing sulphur oxide emissions from vehicles.

Straight vegetable oil

Straight vegetable oil (SVO)[4] is a potential fuel for diesel engines that can be produced from a variety of sources, including oilseed crops such as rapeseed, sunflower, soybean and palm. Used cooking oil from restaurants and animal fat from meat-processing industries can also be used as fuel for diesel vehicles.

Biofuel feedstocks

There are many supply sources of biomass for energy purposes, scattered across large and diverse geographical areas. Even today, most energy derived from biomass used as fuel originates from by-products or co-products of food, fodder and fibre production. For instance, the main by-products of forest industries are used to produce fuelwood and charcoal, and black liquor (a by-product of pulp mills) is a major fuel source for bioelectricity generation in countries such as Brazil, Canada, Finland, Sweden and the United States of America. A considerable amount of heat and power is derived from recovered and/or recycled woody biomass and increasing amounts of energy are recovered from biomass derived from cropland (straw and cotton stalks) and forest land (wood chips and pellets). In sugar- and coffee-producing countries, bagasse and coffee husks are used for direct combustion and to produce heat energy and steam.

In terms of bioenergy, however, the big growth area in recent years has been in the production of liquid biofuels for transport using agricultural crops as feedstocks. The bulk of this has taken the form of ethanol, based on either sugar crops or starchy crops, or biodiesel based on oil crops.

As shown in Figure 6, a range of different crops can be used as feedstock for ethanol and biodiesel production. However, most global ethanol production is derived from sugar cane or maize; in Brazil, the bulk of ethanol is produced from sugar cane and in the United States of America from maize.

---

[4] Also referred to as pure plant oil (PPO).

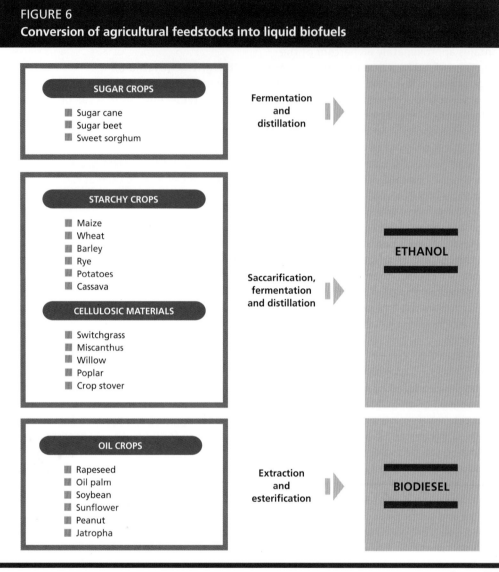

FIGURE 6
Conversion of agricultural feedstocks into liquid biofuels

Source: FAO.

Other significant crops include cassava, rice, sugar beet and wheat. For biodiesel, the most popular feedstocks are rapeseed in the EU, soybean in the United States of America and Brazil, and palm, coconut and castor oils in tropical and subtropical countries, with a growing interest in jatropha.

Biofuels and agriculture

The current expansion and growth of energy markets, as a result of new energy and environment policies enacted over the past decade in most developed countries and in several developing countries, is reshaping the role of agriculture. Most

significant is the sector's increasing role as a provider of feedstock for the production of liquid biofuels for transport – ethanol and biodiesel. Modern bioenergy represents a new source of demand for farmers' products. It thus holds promise for the creation of income and employment. At the same time, it generates increasing competition for natural resources, notably land and water, especially in the short run, although yield increases may mitigate such competition in the longer run. Competition for land becomes an issue especially when some of the crops (e.g. maize, oil palm and soybean) that are currently cultivated for food and feed are redirected towards the production of biofuels, or when food-oriented agricultural land is converted to biofuel production.

Currently, around 85 percent of the global production of liquid biofuels is in the form of ethanol (Table 1). The two largest ethanol producers, Brazil and the United States of America, account for almost 90 percent of total production, with the remainder accounted for mostly by Canada, China, the EU (mainly France and Germany) and India. Biodiesel production is principally concentrated in the EU (with around 60 percent of the total), with a significantly smaller contribution coming from the United States of America. In Brazil, biodiesel production is a more recent phenomenon and production volume remains limited. Other significant biodiesel producers include China, India, Indonesia and Malaysia.

Different crops vary widely in terms of biofuel yield per hectare, both across feedstocks and across countries and production systems, as illustrated in Table 2. Variations are due both to differences in crop yields per hectare across crops and countries and to differences in conversion efficiency across crops. This implies vastly different land requirements for increased biofuel production depending on the crop and location. Currently, ethanol production from sugar cane and sugar beet has the highest yields, with sugar-cane-based production in Brazil

topping the list of in terms of biofuel output per hectare and India not far behind. Yields per hectare are somewhat lower for maize, but with marked differences between yields, for example, in China and in the United States of America. The data reported in Table 2 refer only to technical yields. The cost of producing biofuels based on different crops in different countries may show very different patterns. This is discussed further in Chapter 3.

The biofuels life cycle: energy balances and greenhouse gas emissions

Two of the main driving forces behind policies promoting biofuel development have been concerns over energy security and a desire to reduce greenhouse gas emissions. Just as different crops have different yields in terms of biofuel per hectare, wide variations also occur in terms of energy balance and greenhouse gas emission reductions across feedstocks, locations and technologies.

The contribution of a biofuel to energy supply depends both on the energy content of the biofuel and on the energy going into its production. The latter includes the energy required to cultivate and harvest the feedstock, to process the feedstock into biofuel and to transport the feedstock and

TABLE 1
Biofuel production by country, 2007

COUNTRY/COUNTRY GROUPING	ETHANOL		BIODIESEL		TOTAL	
	(Million litres)	*(Mtoe)*	*(Million litres)*	*(Mtoe)*	*(Million litres)*	*(Mtoe)*
Brazil	19 000	10.44	227	0.17	19 227	10.60
Canada	1 000	0.55	97	0.07	1 097	0.62
China	1 840	1.01	114	0.08	1 954	1.09
India	400	0.22	45	0.03	445	0.25
Indonesia	0	0.00	409	0.30	409	0.30
Malaysia	0	0.00	330	0.24	330	0.24
United States of America	26 500	14.55	1 688	1.25	28 188	15.80
European Union	2 253	1.24	6 109	4.52	8 361	5.76
Others	1 017	0.56	1 186	0.88	2 203	1.44
World	**52 009**	**28.57**	**10 204**	**7.56**	**62 213**	**36.12**

Note: Data presented are subject to rounding.
Source: based on F.O. Licht, 2007, data from the OECD–FAO AgLink-Cosimo database.

TABLE 2
Biofuel yields for different feedstocks and countries

CROP	GLOBAL/NATIONAL ESTIMATES	BIOFUEL	CROP YIELD	CONVERSION EFFICIENCY	BIOFUEL YIELD
			(Tonnes/ha)	*(Litres/tonne)*	*(Litres/ha)*
Sugar beet	Global	Ethanol	46.0	110	5 060
Sugar cane	Global	Ethanol	65.0	70	4 550
Cassava	Global	Ethanol	12.0	180	2 070
Maize	Global	Ethanol	4.9	400	1 960
Rice	Global	Ethanol	4.2	430	1 806
Wheat	Global	Ethanol	2.8	340	952
Sorghum	Global	Ethanol	1.3	380	494
Sugar cane	Brazil	Ethanol	73.5	74.5	5 476
Sugar cane	India	Ethanol	60.7	74.5	4 522
Oil palm	Malaysia	Biodiesel	20.6	230	4 736
Oil palm	Indonesia	Biodiesel	17.8	230	4 092
Maize	United States of America	Ethanol	9.4	399	3 751
Maize	China	Ethanol	5.0	399	1 995
Cassava	Brazil	Ethanol	13.6	137	1 863
Cassava	Nigeria	Ethanol	10.8	137	1 480
Soybean	United States of America	Biodiesel	2.7	205	552
Soybean	Brazil	Biodiesel	2.4	205	491

Sources: Rajagopal *et al.*, 2007, for global data; Naylor *et al.*, 2007, for national data.

the resulting biofuel at the various phases of its production and distribution. The fossil energy balance expresses the ratio of energy contained in the biofuel relative to the fossil energy used in its production. A fossil energy balance of 1.0 means that it requires as much energy to produce a litre of biofuel as it contains; in other words, the biofuel provides no net energy gain or loss. A fossil fuel energy balance of 2.0 means that a litre of biofuel contains twice the amount of energy as that required in its production. Problems in assessing energy balances accurately derive from the difficulty of clearly defining the system boundary for the analysis.

Figure 7 summarizes the results of several studies on fossil energy balances for different types of fuel, as reported by the Worldwatch Institute (2006). The figure reveals wide variations in the estimated fossil energy balances across feedstocks and fuels and,

sometimes, for a feedstock/fuel combination, depending on factors such as feedstock productivity, agricultural practices and conversion technologies.

Conventional petrol and diesel have fossil energy balances of around 0.8–0.9, because some energy is consumed in refining crude oil into usable fuel and transporting it to markets. If a biofuel has a fossil energy balance exceeding these numbers, it contributes to reducing dependence on fossil fuels. All biofuels appear to make a positive contribution in this regard, albeit to widely varying degrees. Estimated fossil fuel balances for biodiesel range from around 1 to 4 for rapeseed and soybean feedstocks. Estimated balances for palm oil are higher, around 9, because other oilseeds must be crushed before the oil can be extracted, an additional processing step that requires energy. For crop-based ethanol, the estimated

FIGURE 7
Estimated ranges of fossil energy balances of selected fuel types

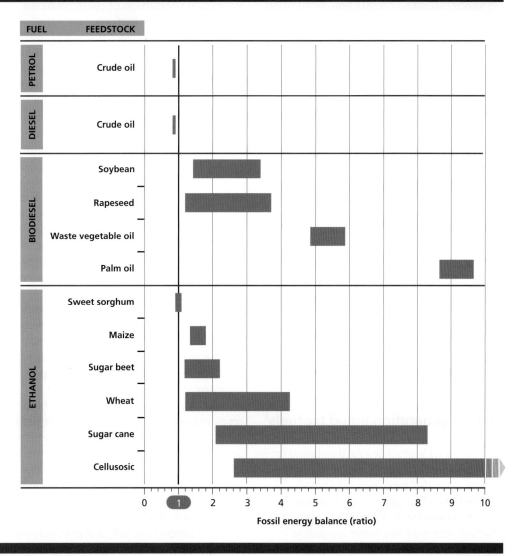

Note: The ratios for cellulosic biofuels are theoretical.

Sources: based on Worldwatch Institute, 2006, Table 10.1; Rajagopal and Zilberman, 2007.

balances range from less than 2 for maize to around 2–8 for sugar cane. The favourable fossil energy balance of sugar-cane-based ethanol, as produced in Brazil, depends not only on feedstock productivity, but also on the fact that it is processed using biomass residues from the sugar cane (bagasse) as energy input. The range of estimated fossil fuel balances for cellulosic feedstocks is even wider, reflecting the uncertainty regarding this technology and the diversity of potential feedstocks and production systems.

Similarly, the net effect of biofuels on greenhouse gas emissions may differ widely.

Biofuels are produced from biomass; in theory, therefore, they should be carbon neutral, as their combustion only returns to the atmosphere the carbon that was sequestered from the atmosphere by the plant during its growth – unlike fossil fuels, which release carbon that has been stored for millions of years under the surface of the earth. However, assessing the net effect of a biofuel on greenhouse gas emissions requires analysis of emissions throughout the life cycle of the biofuel: planting and harvesting the crop; processing the feedstock into biofuel; transporting the feedstock and the final fuel; and storing, distributing and retailing the biofuel – including the impacts of fuelling a vehicle and the emissions caused by combustion. In addition, any possible co-products that may reduce emissions need to be considered. Clearly, therefore, fossil energy balances are only one of several determinants of the emissions impact of biofuels. Critical factors related to the agricultural production process include fertilizing, pesticide use, irrigation technology and soil treatment. Land-use changes associated with expanded biofuel production can have a major impact. For example, converting forest land to the production of biofuel crops or agricultural crops displaced by biofuel feedstocks elsewhere can release large quantities of carbon that would take years to recover through the emission reductions achieved by substituting biofuels for fossil fuels. Chapter 5 discusses further the relationship between biofuels and greenhouse gas emissions and reviews the evidence that the impact of biofuels on climate change may vary and may not necessarily be positive – or as positive as is often initially assumed.

Second-generation liquid biofuels[5]

Current liquid biofuel production based on sugar and starch crops (for ethanol) and oilseed crops (for biodiesel) is generally referred to as first-generation biofuels. A second generation of technologies under development may also make it possible to use lignocellulosic biomass. Cellulosic biomass is more resistant to being broken down than starch, sugar and oils. The difficulty of converting it into liquid fuels makes the conversion technology more expensive, although the cost of the cellulosic feedstock itself is lower than for current, first-generation feedstocks. Conversion of cellulose to ethanol involves two steps: the cellulose and hemicellulose components of the biomass are first broken down into sugars, which are then fermented to obtain ethanol. The first step is technically challenging, although research continues

on developing efficient and cost-effective ways of carrying out the process. The lack of commercial viability has so far inhibited significant production of cellulose-based second-generation biofuels.

As cellulosic biomass is the most abundant biological material on earth, the successful development of commercially viable second-generation cellulose-based biofuels could significantly expand the volume and variety of feedstocks that can be used for production. Cellulosic wastes, including waste products from agriculture (straw, stalks, leaves) and forestry, wastes generated from processing (nut shells, sugar-cane bagasse, sawdust) and organic parts of municipal waste, could all be potential sources. However, it is also important to consider the crucial role that decomposing biomass plays in maintaining soil fertility and texture; excessive withdrawals for bioenergy use could have negative effects.

Dedicated cellulosic energy crops hold promise as a source of feedstock for second-generation technologies. Potential crops include short-rotation woody crops such as willow, hybrid poplars and eucalyptus or grassy species such as miscanthus, switchgrass and reed canary grass. These crops present major advantages over first-generation crops in terms of environmental sustainability. Compared with conventional starch and oilseed crops, they can produce more biomass per hectare of land because the entire crop is available as feedstock for conversion to fuel. Furthermore, some fast-growing perennials such as short-rotation woody crops and tall grasses can sometimes grow on poor, degraded soils where food-crop production is not optimal because of erosion or other limitations. Both these factors may reduce competition for land with food and feed production. On the downside, several of these species are considered invasive or potentially invasive and may have negative impacts on water resources, biodiversity and agriculture.

Second-generation feedstocks and biofuels could also offer advantages in terms of reducing greenhouse gas emissions. Most studies project that future, advanced fuels from perennial crops and woody and agricultural residues could dramatically reduce life-cycle greenhouse gas emissions

---

[5] This section is based on GBEP (2007), IEA (2004) and Rutz and Janssen (2007).

relative to petroleum fuels and first-generation biofuels. This stems from both the higher energy yields per hectare and the different choice of fuel used in the conversion process. In the current production process for ethanol, the energy used in processing is almost universally supplied by fossil fuels (with the exception of sugar-cane-based ethanol in Brazil, where most of the energy for conversion is provided by sugar-cane bagasse). For second-generation biofuels, process energy could be provided by left-over parts of the plants (mainly lignin).

While cellulosic biomass is harder to break down for conversion to liquid fuels, it is also more robust for handling, thus helping to reduce its handling costs and maintain its quality compared with food crops. It is also easier to store, especially in comparison with sugar-based crops, as it resists deterioration. On the other hand, cellulosic biomass can often be bulky and would require a well-developed transportation infrastructure for delivery to processing plants after harvest.

Significant technological challenges still need to be overcome to make the production of ethanol from lignocellulosic feedstocks commercially competitive. It is still uncertain when conversion of cellulosic biomass into advanced fuels may be able to contribute a significant proportion of the world's liquid fuels. Currently, there are a number of pilot and demonstration plants either operating or under development around the world. The speed of expansion of biochemical and thermochemical conversion pathways will depend upon the development and success of pilot projects currently under way and sustained research funding, as well as world oil prices and private-sector investment.

In summary, second-generation biofuels based on lignocellulosic feedstocks present a completely different picture in terms of their implications for agriculture and food security. A much wider variety of feedstocks could be used, beyond the agricultural crops currently used for first-generation technologies, and with higher energy yields per hectare. Their effects on commodity markets, land-use change and the environment will also differ – as will their influence over future production and transformation technologies (see Box 2).

Potential for bioenergy

What is the potential for bioenergy production? The technical and economic potential for bioenergy should be discussed in the context of the increasing shocks and stress on the global agriculture sector and the growing demand for food and agricultural products that is a consequence of continuing population and income growth worldwide. What is technically feasible to produce may not be economically feasible or environmentally sustainable. This section discusses in more detail the technical and economic potential of bioenergy.

Because bioenergy is derived from biomass, global bioenergy potential is ultimately limited by the total amount of energy produced by global photosynthesis. Plants collect a total energy equivalent of about 75 000 Mtoe (3 150 Exajoule) per year (Kapur, 2004) – or six to seven times the current global energy demand. However, this includes vast amounts of biomass that cannot be harvested. In purely physical terms, biomass represents a relatively poor way of harvesting solar energy, particularly when compared with increasingly efficient solar panels (FAO, 2006a).

A number of studies have gauged the volume of biomass that can technically contribute to global energy supplies. Their estimates differ widely owing to different scopes, assumptions and methodologies, underscoring the high degree of uncertainty surrounding the possible contribution of bioenergy to future global energy supply. The last major study of bioenergy conducted by the International Energy Agency (IEA) assessed, on the basis of existing studies, the range of potential bioenergy supply in 2050 from a low of 1 000 Mtoe to an extreme of 26 200 Mtoe (IEA, 2006, pp. 412–16). The latter figure was based on an assumption of very rapid technological progress; however, the IEA indicates that a more realistic assessment based on slower yield improvements would be 6 000–12 000 Mtoe. A mid-range estimate of around 9 500 Mtoe would, according to the IEA, require about one-fifth of the world's agricultural land to be dedicated to biomass production.

BOX 2
Biotechnology applications for biofuels

Many existing biotechnologies can be applied to improve bioenergy production, for example, in developing better biomass feedstocks and improving the efficiency of converting the biomass to biofuels.

Biotechnologies for first-generation biofuels
The plant varieties currently used for first-generation biofuel production have been selected for agronomic traits relevant for food and/or feed production and not for characteristics that favour their use as feedstocks for biofuel production. Biotechnology can help to speed up the selection of varieties that are more suited to biofuel production – with increased biomass per hectare, increased content of oils (biodiesel crops) or fermentable sugars (ethanol crops), or improved processing characteristics that facilitate their conversion to biofuels. The field of genomics – the study of all the genetic material of an organism (its genome) – is likely to play an increasingly important role. Genome sequences of several first-generation feedstocks, such as maize, sorghum and soybean, are in the pipeline or have already been published. Apart from genomics, other biotechnologies that can be applied include marker-assisted selection and genetic modification.

Fermentation of sugars is central to the production of ethanol from biomass. However, the most commonly used industrial fermentation micro-organism, the yeast *Saccharomyces cerevisiae*, cannot directly ferment starchy material, such as maize starch. The biomass must first be broken down (hydrolysed) to fermentable sugars using enzymes called amylases. Many of the current commercially available enzymes, including amylases, are produced using genetically modified micro-organisms. Research continues on developing efficient genetic yeast strains that can produce the amylases themselves, so that the hydrolysis and fermentation steps can be combined.

Application of biotechnologies for second-generation biofuels
Lignocellulosic biomass consists mainly of lignin and the polysaccharides cellulose (consisting of hexose sugars) and hemicellulose (containing a mix of hexose and pentose sugars). Compared with the production of ethanol from first-generation feedstocks, the use of lignocellulosic biomass is more complicated because the polysaccharides are more stable and the pentose sugars are not readily fermentable by *Saccharomyces cerevisiae*. In order to convert lignocellulosic biomass to biofuels the polysaccharides must first be hydrolysed, or broken down, into simple sugars using either acid or enzymes. Several biotechnology-based approaches are being used to overcome such problems, including the development of strains of *Saccharomyces cerevisiae* that can ferment pentose sugars, the use of alternative yeast species that naturally ferment pentose sugars, and the engineering of enzymes that are able to break down cellulose and hemicellulose into simple sugars.

Apart from agricultural, forestry and other by-products, the main source of lignocellulosic biomass for second-generation biofuels is likely to be from "dedicated biomass feedstocks", such as certain perennial grass and forest tree species. Genomics, genetic modification and other biotechnologies are all being investigated as tools to produce plants with desirable characteristics for second-generation biofuel production, for example plants that produce less lignin (a compound that cannot be fermented into liquid biofuel), that produce enzymes themselves for cellulose and/or lignin degradation, or that produce increased cellulose or overall biomass yields.

Sources: based on FAO, 2007a, and The Royal Society, 2008.

More important than the purely technical viability is the question of how much of the technically available bioenergy potential would be economically viable. The long-term economic potential depends crucially on assumptions concerning the prices of fossil energy, the development of agricultural feedstocks and future technological innovations in harvesting, converting and using biofuels. These aspects are discussed in further detail in Chapter 3.

A different way of looking at the potential for biofuel production is to consider the relative land-use requirements. In its "Reference Scenario" for 2030 in *World Energy Outlook 2006*, the IEA projects an increase in the share of the world's arable land devoted to growing biomass for liquid biofuels from 1 percent in 2004 to 2.5 percent in 2030. Under its "Alternative Policy Scenario", the share in 2030 increases to 3.8 percent. In both cases, the projections are based on the assumption that liquid biofuels will be produced using conventional crops. Should second-generation liquid biofuels become widely commercialized before 2030, the IEA projects the global share of biofuels in transport demand to increase to 10 percent rather than 3 percent in its Reference Scenario and 5 percent in the Alternative Policy Scenario. Land-use requirements would go up only slightly, to 4.2 percent of arable land, because of higher energy yields per hectare and the use of waste biomass for fuel

production. Nevertheless, this illustrates that, even under a second-generation scenario, a hypothetical large-scale substitution of liquid biofuels for fossil-fuel-based petrol would require major conversion of land. See also Chapter 4 for a further discussion, including regional impacts.

The potential for current biofuel technologies to replace fossil fuels is also illustrated by a hypothetical calculation by Rajagopal *et al.* (2007). They report theoretical estimates for global ethanol production from the main cereal and sugar crops based on global average yields and commonly reported conversion efficiencies. The results of their estimates are summarized in Table 3. The crops shown account for 42 percent of total cropland today. Conversion of the entire crop production to ethanol would correspond to 57 percent of total petrol consumption. Under a more realistic assumption of 25 percent of each of these crops being diverted to ethanol production, only 14 percent of petrol consumption could be replaced by ethanol. The various hypothetical calculations underline that, in view of their significant land requirements, biofuels can only be expected to lead to a very limited displacement of fossil fuels. Nevertheless, even a very modest contribution of biofuels to overall energy supply may yet have a strong impact on agriculture and on agricultural markets.

TABLE 3
Hypothetical potential for ethanol from principal cereal and sugar crops

CROP	GLOBAL AREA	GLOBAL PRODUCTION	BIOFUEL YIELD	MAXIMUM ETHANOL	PETROL EQUIVALENT	SUPPLY AS SHARE OF 2003 GLOBAL PETROL USE[1]
	(Million ha)	*(Million tonnes)*	*(Litres/ha)*	*(Billion litres)*	*(Billion litres)*	*(Percentage)*
Wheat	215	602	952	205	137	12
Rice	150	630	1 806	271	182	16
Maize	145	711	1 960	284	190	17
Sorghum	45	59	494	22	15	1
Sugar cane	20	1 300	4 550	91	61	6
Cassava	19	219	2 070	39	26	2
Sugar beet	5.4	248	5 060	27	18	2
Total	599	...	...	940	630	57

Note: ... = not applicable. Data presented are subject to rounding.
[1] Global petrol use in 2003 = 1 100 billion litres (Kim and Dale, 2004).
Source: Rajapogal *et al.*, 2007.

Key messages of the chapter

- Bioenergy covers approximately 10 percent of total world energy supply. Traditional unprocessed biomass accounts for most of this, but commercial bioenergy is assuming greater importance.
- Liquid biofuels for transport are generating the most attention and have seen a rapid expansion in production. However, quantitatively their role is only marginal: they cover 1 percent of total transport fuel consumption and 0.2–0.3 percent of total energy consumption worldwide.
- The main liquid biofuels are ethanol and biodiesel. Both can be produced from a wide range of different feedstocks. The most important producers are Brazil and the United States of America for ethanol and the EU for biodiesel.
- Current technologies for liquid biofuels rely on agricultural commodities as feedstock. Ethanol is based on sugar or starchy crops, with sugar cane in Brazil and maize in the United States of America being the most significant in terms of volume. Biodiesel is produced using a range of different oil crops.
- Large-scale production of biofuels implies large land requirements for feedstock production. Liquid biofuels can therefore be expected to displace fossil fuels for transport to only a very limited extent.
- Even though liquid biofuels supply only a small share of global energy needs, they still have the potential to have a significant effect on global agriculture and agricultural markets because of the volume of feedstocks and the relative land areas needed for their production.
- The contribution of different biofuels to reducing fossil-fuel consumption varies widely when the fossil energy used as an input in their production is also taken into account. The fossil energy balance of a biofuel depends on factors such as feedstock characteristics, production location, agricultural practices and the source of energy used for the conversion process. Different biofuels also perform very differently in terms of their contribution to reducing greenhouse gas emissions.
- Second-generation biofuels currently under development would use lignocellulosic feedstocks such as wood, tall grasses, and forestry and crop residues. This would increase the quantitative potential for biofuel generation per hectare of land and could also improve the fossil energy and greenhouse gas balances of biofuels. However, it is not known when such technologies will enter production on a significant commercial scale.

3. Economic and policy drivers of liquid biofuels

Agriculture both supplies and demands energy; hence, markets in both sectors have always been linked. The nature and strength of these linkages have changed over the years, but agricultural and energy markets have always adjusted to each other, with output and consumption rising or falling in response to changing relative prices. Rapidly increasing demand for liquid biofuels is now tying agriculture and energy more closely than ever. However, policy plays an influential role in defining the linkages between them. Many countries intervene in both markets through a range of policy measures aimed at addressing a diverse range of goals. This chapter addresses the fundamental economic relationships among agriculture, energy and biofuels. It also reviews the policies being pursued to promote biofuels and discusses the way in which they affect the relationship between agricultural and energy markets.

Biofuel markets and policies

A discussion of the economics of liquid biofuels must start from the allocation of resources among competing uses in the energy and agriculture sectors. This competition occurs at several levels. In energy markets, liquid biofuels such as ethanol and biodiesel are direct competitors with petroleum-based petrol and diesel. Policies such as mandated blending of biofuels with petrol and diesel, subsidies and tax incentives can encourage biofuel use, while technical constraints such as a lack of vehicles that run on biofuel blends can discourage their use. Leaving aside such factors for the moment, biofuels and fossil fuels compete on the basis of their energy content, and their prices generally move together.

In agricultural markets, biofuel processors compete directly with food processors and animal-feeding operations for commodities.

From the point of view of an individual farmer, it is unimportant what end use a prospective buyer has in mind for the crop. Farmers will sell to an ethanol or biodiesel processor if the price they receive is higher than they could obtain from a food processor or a feeding operation. If the price of biofuels is high enough, it will bid agricultural commodities away from other uses. Because energy markets are large relative to agricultural markets, a small change in energy demand can imply a large change in demand for agricultural feedstocks. Therefore crude oil prices will drive biofuel prices and, in turn, influence agricultural commodity prices.

The close link between crude oil prices and agricultural prices, mediated by biofuel demand, in fact establishes a floor and a ceiling for prices of agricultural commodities – determined by crude oil prices (FAO, 2006a). When fossil fuel prices reach or exceed the cost of producing substitute biofuels, the energy market creates demand for agricultural products. If the demand for energy is high relative to markets for agricultural commodities and agricultural biofuel feedstocks are competitive in the energy market, this will create a floor price effect for agricultural products determined by fossil fuel prices. At the same time, however, agricultural prices cannot increase faster than energy prices or they will price themselves out of the energy market. Thus, as energy markets are very large compared with agricultural markets, agricultural prices will tend to be driven by energy prices.

In practice, the link between energy and agricultural commodity prices may be less close and immediate than in theory, at least until biofuel markets become sufficiently developed. In the short run, a number of constraints limit the capacity of the biofuel sector to respond to changes in relative prices of fossil fuels and agricultural commodities, for example bottlenecks in distribution, technical problems in

BOX 3
Biofuel policies in Brazil

Around 45 percent of all energy consumed in Brazil comes from renewable sources, reflecting the combined use of hydroelectricity (14.5 percent) and biomass (30.1 percent); the use of sugar cane in the internal renewable energy supply in 2006 represented 32.2 percent of renewable energy and 14.5 percent of total internal energy supply (GBEP, 2007).

Brazil has been a pioneer in national regulatory efforts for the bioenergy sector and has accumulated significant experience and expertise in the area of biofuels, particularly concerning the use of ethanol as a transport fuel. The Brazilian experience of using ethanol as a petrol additive dates back to the 1920s, but it was only in 1931 that fuel produced from sugar cane officially began to be blended with petrol. In 1975, following the first oil crisis, the Government launched the National Ethanol Programme (ProAlcool), creating the conditions for large-scale development of the sugar and ethanol industry. The programme was aimed at reducing energy imports and fostering energy independence. Its main goals were to introduce into the market a mixture of petrol and anhydrous ethanol and to provide incentives for the development of vehicles that were fuelled exclusively with hydrated ethanol. Following the second major oil shock, in 1979, a more ambitious and comprehensive programme was implemented, promoting the

development of new plantations and a fleet of purely ethanol-fuelled vehicles. A series of tax and financial incentives was introduced. The programme induced a strong response, with ethanol production rising rapidly along with the number of vehicles running exclusively on ethanol.

Subsidies provided through the programme were intended to be temporary, as high oil prices were expected to make ethanol competitive with petrol in the long run. However, as international oil prices fell in 1986, the elimination of subsidies became problematic. In addition, rising sugar prices led to scarcity of ethanol, and in 1989 severe shortages in some of the main consuming centres undermined the credibility of the programme.

The period from 1989 to 2000 was characterized by the dismantling of the set of government economic incentives for the programme as part of a broader deregulation that affected Brazil's entire fuel supply system. In 1990, the Sugar and Ethanol Institute, which had regulated the Brazilian sugar and ethanol industry for over six decades, was extinguished, and the planning and implementation of the industry's production, distribution and sales activities were gradually transferred to the private sector. With the end of the subsidies, the use of hydrated ethanol as fuel diminished drastically. However, the mixture of anhydrous ethanol with petrol

transportation and blending systems or inadequate plant capacity for conversion of feedstocks. The more flexibly demand and supply can respond to changing price signals, the more closely prices on energy and agricultural markets will be linked. Today, the Brazilian sugar-cane ethanol market is the most developed and most closely integrated with energy markets. Contributory factors include the existence of a large number of sugar mills able to produce either sugar or ethanol, highly efficient energy conversion systems with co-generation of ethanol and electricity, a large share of flex-fuel vehicles

capable of running on ethanol–petrol blends and a national distribution network for ethanol (FAO, 2006a).

While agricultural feedstocks compete with fossil fuels on the energy market, agricultural crops also compete with each other for productive resources. For example, a given plot of land can be used to grow maize for ethanol or wheat for bread. When biofuel demand bids up the prices of commodities used as biofuel feedstock, this tends to bid up the prices of all agricultural commodities that rely on the same resource base. For this reason, producing biofuels from non-

TABLE 4
Voluntary and mandatory bioenergy targets for transport fuels in G8+5 countries

COUNTRY/COUNTRY GROUPING	TARGETS[1]
Brazil	Mandatory blend of 20–25 percent anhydrous ethanol with petrol; minimum blending of 3 percent biodiesel to diesel by July 2008 and 5 percent (B5) by end of 2010
Canada	5 percent renewable content in petrol by 2010 and 2 percent renewable content in diesel fuel by 2012
China	15 percent of transport energy needs through use of biofuels by 2020
France	5.75 percent by 2008, 7 percent by 2010, 10 percent by 2015 (V), 10 percent by 2020 (M = EU target)
Germany	6.75 percent by 2010, set to rise to 8 percent by 2015, 10 percent by 2020 (M = EU target)
India	Proposed blending mandates of 5–10 percent for ethanol and 20 percent for biodiesel
Italy	5.75 percent by 2010 (M), 10 percent by 2020 (M = EU target)
Japan	500 000 kilolitres, as converted to crude oil, by 2010 (V)
Mexico	Targets under consideration
Russian Federation	No targets
South Africa	Up to 8 percent by 2006 (V) (10 percent target under consideration)
United Kingdom	5 percent biofuels by 2010 (M), 10 percent by 2020 (M = EU target)
United States of America	9 billion gallons by 2008, rising to 36 billion by 2022 (M). Of the 36 billion gallons, 21 billion to be from advanced biofuels (of which 16 billion from cellulosic biofuels)
European Union	10 percent by 2020 (M proposed by EU Commission in January 2008)

[1] M = mandatory; V = voluntary.

Sources: GBEP, 2007, updated with information from the United States Department of Agriculture (USDA, 2008a), the Renewable Fuels Association (RFA, 2008) and written communication from the EU Commission and Professor Ricardo Abramovay, University of São Paulo, Brazil.

TABLE 5
Applied tariffs on ethanol in selected countries

Country/Country grouping	Applied MFN tariff	At pre-tariff unit value of US$0.50/litre		Exceptions/Comments
	Local currency or ad valorem rate	Ad valorem equivalent	Specific-rate equivalent	
		(Percentage)	*(US$/litre)*	
Australia	5 percent + A$0.38143/litre	51	0.34	United States of America, New Zealand
Brazil	0 percent	0	0.00	From 20 percent in March 2006
Canada	Can$0.0492/litre	9	0.047	FTA partners
Switzerland	SwF35/100 kg	46	0.232	EU, GSP
United States of America	2.5 percent + US$0.54/gallon	28	0.138	FTA partners, CBI partners
European Union	€0.192/litre	52	0.26	EFTA, GSP

Notes: Ethanol is classified for trade purposes as HS 2207.10, undenatured ethyl alcohol.
Tariffs indicated are rates as of 1 January 2007.
MFN = most-favoured nation; FTA = Free Trade Association; EFTA = European Free Trade Association;
GSP = Generalised System of Preferences; CBI = Caribbean Basin Initiative.
Source: Steenblik, 2007.

BOX 4
Biofuel policies in the United States of America

The production of ethanol from maize currently dominates United States biofuel production, with production levels of 30 billion litres in 2007, followed by biodiesel from soybean, which reached 2 billion litres. The United States of America is also devoting significant resources towards developing and implementing next-generation biofuel technologies.

A range of policies are currently being implemented to promote bioenergy, including the Energy Policy Act of 2005, the Energy Independence and Security Act of 2007, the 2002 Farm Bill and the Biomass Research and Development Act of 2000. Several of these affect liquid biofuels for transport.

Financial incentives to biofuels began during the Carter Administration with the 1978 Energy Tax Act, following the oil price shocks of the 1970s. The Act provided an excise tax exemption for alcohol fuel blends at 100 percent of the petrol tax, which at the time was 4 cents per gallon. More recently, the American Jobs Creation Act of 2004 introduced the Volumetric Ethanol Excise Tax Credit (VEETC), a tax credit of 51 cents per gallon of ethanol for blenders and retailers. The VEETC was extended by the 2005 Energy Policy Act through to 2010, and was expanded to include biodiesel. Biodiesel producers who use agricultural feedstocks are eligible for a tax credit of US$1.00 per gallon, while producers of waste-grease biodiesel can receive a credit of 50 cents per gallon. Several states also offer some form of excise tax exemptions. VEETC is applied to biofuels regardless of their country of origin. However, a 54 cents/gallon and 2.5 percent ad valorem tariff is imposed on imported ethanol.

The Energy Policy Act of 2005 introduced quantitative targets for renewable fuels. Indeed, the Renewable Fuels Standard (RFS), established by the Act, mandated that all motor petrol sold in the United States of America must have reached a renewable fuel content of 7.5 billion gallons (1 gallon = 3.785 litres) by 2012; after 2012, the percentage content was to be maintained at the level of 2012. Several states have also

incentives or penalties are among the most widely used instruments and can dramatically affect the competitiveness of biofuels *vis-à-vis* other energy sources and thus their commercial viability. The United States of America was among the first of the OECD countries to implement biofuel tax exemptions with the 1978 Energy Tax Act, following the oil price shocks of the 1970s. The Act provided an excise tax exemption for alcohol fuel blends. In 2004, the tax exemption was replaced by an income tax credit for producers. Other countries have since implemented different forms of excise tax exemptions.

Research and development
Most biofuel-producing countries conduct or fund research and development at various stages of the biofuel production process, ranging from agronomy to combustion.

Bioenergy research and development has generally been aimed at developing technologies for improving conversion efficiency, identifying sustainable feedstock and developing cost-effective conversion methods for advanced fuels. Current patterns of funding in developed countries suggest that an increasing proportion of public research and development funding is directed towards second-generation biofuels, in particular cellulosic ethanol and biomass-derived alternatives to petroleum-based diesel.

Economic costs of biofuel policies

The Global Subsidies Initiative (Steenblik, 2007) has prepared estimates of subsidies to the biofuel sector in selected OECD economies, presented in Table 6. These

implemented, or plan to implement, their own renewable fuels standards.

The 2005 Act also continued funding for the Biomass Program, providing more than US$500 million to promote use of biotechnology and other advanced processes to make biofuels from cellulosic feedstocks cost-competitive with petrol and diesel, to increase the production of bioproducts that reduce the use of fossil fuels in manufacturing facilities and to demonstrate the commercial application of integrated bio-refineries that use cellulosic feedstocks to produce liquid transport fuels, high-value chemicals, electricity and heat.

The Energy Independence and Security Act of 2007 established more ambitious quantitative targets, stipulating a volume for 2008 of 9 billion gallons of renewable fuels and a phased increase to 36 billion gallons by 2022. Of the latter, 21 billion gallons should be covered by advanced biofuels (of which 16 billion from cellulosic biofuels and 5 billion from undifferentiated advanced biofuels).

In terms of grants, the 2007 Energy Independence and Security Act authorized US$500 million annually for the fiscal years 2008–15 for the production of advanced biofuels with at least an 80 percent reduction in life-cycle greenhouse gas emissions relative to current fuels. It likewise foresaw a US$200 million grant programme for the installation of refuelling infrastructure for ethanol-85.

The 2002 Farm Bill had included several provisions to promote the development of bio-refineries, to provide incentives to feedstock producers and to realize education programmes for farmers, local authorities and civil society promoting the benefits of biofuel production and utilization. The 2007 Farm Bill, voted by Congress in May 2008, reduced the tax credit for maize-based ethanol from 51 to 45 cents per gallon and introduced a tax credit of US$1.01 per gallon for cellulose-based ethanol.

Sources: based on GBEP, 2007, and information from USDA, 2008a, and RFA, 2008.

estimates give a rough idea of the magnitude of transfers supporting biofuels in the countries covered, although they probably tend to underestimate the total value of investment incentives, for which information is difficult to obtain. The estimates do not consider potential market-distorting impacts of the different policies.

The total support estimates (TSE) calculate the total value of all government support to the biofuels industry including, among others, consumption mandates, tax credits, import barriers, investment subsidies and general support to the sector such as public research investment. They are analogous to the TSE calculated for agriculture by the OECD. As such, they include measures deemed to be directly tied to production levels and less-distorting supports that are not directly linked to output. They do not include support to agricultural feedstock

production, which is calculated separately in the TSE for agriculture.

Table 6 confirms that biofuel subsidies are already relatively costly for taxpayers and consumers in the OECD economies, with United States processors and growers receiving support worth just over US$6 billion per year, and those in the EU receiving almost US$5 billion per year. The table also provides estimates of the share of TSE that varies according to the level of production. This provides an indication of how the total would change with increasing output, such as that implied by the consumption targets in place in the EU and the United States of America. EU ethanol subsidies are almost completely variable with output and so would increase in line with mandated increases in output. The table also suggests that OECD biofuel subsidies are likely to become much larger as mandated consumption increases.

BOX 5
Biofuel policies in the European Union

Over the past decade, the production and use of biofuels has increased substantially in the European Union (EU). In 2007, 9 billion litres of biofuel were produced, dominated by biodiesel (6 billion litres). The sector has undergone very rapid growth, with Germany accounting for more than half of EU biodiesel production. The main feedstock used is rapeseed (about 80 percent), with sunflower oil and soybean oil making up most of the rest. The EU industry has been slower to invest in ethanol production, which totalled almost 3 billion litres in 2007. The main ethanol feedstocks are sugar beet and cereals.

EU biofuel legislation consists of three main Directives. The first pillar is Directive 2003/30/EC for promotion of a biofuels market in the EU. To encourage biofuel use, in competition with less costly fossil fuels, the Directive sets a voluntary "reference target" of 2 percent biofuel consumption (on the basis of energy content) by 2005 and 5.75 percent by 31 December 2010. It obliges Member

States to set national indicative targets for the share of biofuels, in line with reference percentages of the Directive, although it leaves them free to choose a strategy to achieve these targets.

The second pillar is Directive 2003/96/EC, which allows for the application of tax incentives for biofuels. Taxation not being within the sphere of action of the European Community, each Member State can decide on a level of taxation for fossil fuels and biofuels. However, these tax exemptions are considered as environmental state aid and therefore their implementation by Member States requires authorization from the European Commission in order to avoid undue distortions of competition.

The third pillar of the EU biofuel legislation concerns environmental specifications for fuels indicated in Directive 98/70/EC amended by Directive 2003/17/EC. The Directive contains a 5 percent limit on ethanol blending for environmental reasons. The Commission

TABLE 6
Total support estimates for biofuels in selected OECD economies in 2006

OECD economy	ETHANOL		BIODIESEL		TOTAL LIQUID BIOFUELS	
	TSE	Variable share[1]	TSE	Variable share[1]	TSE	Variable share[1]
	(Billion US$)	(Percentage)	(Billion US$)	(Percentage)	(Billion US$)	(Percentage)
United States of America[2]	5.8	93	0.53	89	6.33	93
European Union[3]	1.6	98	3.1	90	4.7	93
Canada[4]	0.15	70	0.013	55	0.163	69
Australia[5]	0.043	60	0.032	75	0.075	66
Switzerland	0.001	94	0.009	94	0.01	94
Total	7.6	93	3.7	90	11.3	92

[1] The percentage of support that varies with increasing production or consumption, and includes market-price support, production payments or tax credits, fuel-excise tax credits and subsidies to variable inputs.
[2] Lower bound of the reported range.
[3] Total for the 25 Member States of the European Union in 2006.
[4] Provisional estimates.
[5] Data refer to the fiscal year beginning 1 July 2006.

Sources: Steenblik, 2007; Koplow, 2007; Quirke, Steenblik and Warner, 2008.

has proposed an amendment that includes a 10 percent blend for ethanol.

Bioenergy support has also been introduced as part of the Common Agricultural Policy, especially following its reform in 2003. By cutting the link between payments made to farmers and the specific crops they produce, the reform allowed them to take advantage of new market opportunities such as those offered by biofuels. A special aid of €45 per hectare is available for energy crops grown on non-set-aside land (traditional food crop areas). In addition, while farmers cannot cultivate food crops on set-aside land, they can use this land for non-food crops, including biofuels, and are eligible to receive compensatory payments per hectare.

Support to bioenergy comes also from the new EU rural development policy, which includes measures to support renewable energies, such as grants and capital costs for setting up biomass production.

In March 2007, the European Council, based on the Commission's Communication *An energy policy for Europe*, endorsed a binding target of a 20 percent share of renewable energies in overall EU energy consumption by 2020, as well as a 10 percent binding minimum target for the share of biofuels in overall EU petrol and diesel consumption for transport by 2020. The latter target is subject to production being sustainable, second-generation biofuels becoming commercially available and the fuel-quality Directive being amended to allow for adequate levels of blending (Council of the European Union, 2007). A proposal for a renewable energy Directive including both these targets and sustainability criteria for biofuels was put forward by the European Commission to the Council and the European Parliament on 23 January 2008.

Sources: based on GBEP, 2007, and information from the Web site of the European Commission.

To provide some perspective on the relative importance of these biofuel subsidies, Table 7 shows them on a per-litre basis. Ethanol subsidies range from about US$0.30 to US$1.00 per litre, while the range of biodiesel subsidies is wider. The table reveals that although some countries' total support expenditures are relatively modest, they can be substantial on a per-litre basis. Again, the variable portion of support provides an indication of the scope for increases in expenditures as output grows, although some subsidies are budget-limited, especially at the state or provincial levels.

Economic viability of biofuels

The biofuel policies discussed above are shaping the global agricultural economy in ways that may have unintended consequences for the countries implementing the policies and for the rest of the world. All countries are affected, whether or not they produce biofuels. The mandates, subsidies and incentives being implemented by various countries have created a major new source of demand for agricultural commodities. As a consequence, the historic linkages between agriculture and the energy sector are becoming stronger and are changing in character. Biofuel policies have important implications for farm output and incomes, commodity prices and food availability, returns to land and other resources, rural employment and energy markets.

An individual farmer will produce feedstock for biofuels if the net revenue he or she earns is greater than for alternative crops or uses. The decision-making process for a biofuel crop is the same as for any other crop. Farmers choose what to produce on the basis of expected net revenues and perceptions of risk and may use formal models, experience, tradition or a combination of the three in making their choice. The calculus will differ from farm to farm and season to season, depending on the prevailing market and agronomic conditions.

Within the prevailing policy and market context, the price a farmer receives for a biofuel crop depends primarily on the energy potential of the crop, conversion costs, transportation costs and the value of co-products. As discussed in Chapter 2, crops differ in their physical energy potential, which is a function of biomass feedstock yields per hectare and the efficiency with which the feedstock is converted to biofuels. Yields vary from crop to crop, depending on cultivars, agronomic practices, soil quality and weather.

Global average crop yields for first-generation ethanol feedstocks range from 1.3 tonnes per hectare for sweet sorghum to 65 tonnes for sugar cane (see Table 2 on page 16). Similarly, conversion efficiency ranges from 70 litres of ethanol per tonne for sugar cane to 430 litres for rice. In terms of land intensity (litres/hectare), sugar beet and sugar cane are the most productive first-generation crops. Economic efficiency may differ markedly, however, because the costs of production vary widely by crop and location.

Budgeting models can be used to evaluate the financial performance of biofuel processing firms. Tiffany and Eidman (2003) calculated the performance of a dry-mill ethanol plant based on a range of maize prices, ethanol prices, prices of co-products, natural gas prices and interest rates relative to alternative investments. This model found that ethanol plants had experienced great volatility in net returns over the preceding decade and that net returns were highly sensitive to changes in price for maize, ethanol and natural gas. These price changes, together with variations in ethanol yields, could thus have a marked effect on net margins for ethanol plants.

Yu and Tao (2008) provide a simulation of three ethanol projects in different regions of China based on different feedstocks: cassava, wheat and maize. They took into consideration the variability of feedstock and petroleum prices and calculated the expected net present value (NPV) and internal rate of return (IRR) of investments of the three projects under a range of price conditions. They found that the cassava project had a positive expected NPV and an IRR exceeding 12 percent under most scenarios and thus was likely to be economically competitive,

TABLE 7

Approximate average and variable rates of support per litre of biofuel in selected OECD economies

OECD economy	ETHANOL		BIODIESEL	
	Average	Variable	Average	Variable
	(US$/litre)[1]	(US$/litre)[1]	(US$/litre)[1]	(US$/litre)[1]
United States of America[2]	0.28	Federal: 0.15 States: 0.00–0.26	0.55	Federal: 0.26 States: 0.00–26
European Union[3]	1.00	0.00–0.90	0.70	0.00–0.50
Canada[4]	0.40	Federal: up to 0.10 Provinces: 0.00–0.20	0.20	Federal: up to 0.20 Provinces: 0.00–0.14
Australia[5]	0.36	0.32	0.35	0.32
Switzerland[6]	0.60	0.60	1.00	0.60–2.00

Notes:
[1] Values (except in the case of the United States of America and Australia) are rounded to the nearest US$0.10.
[2] Lower bound of reported range. Some payments are budget-limited.
[3] Refers to support provided by Member States.
[4] Provisional estimates; includes incentives introduced on 1 April 2008. Federal and most provincial supports are budget-limited.
[5] Data refer to the fiscal year beginning 1 July 2006. Payments are not budget-limited.
[6] Range for biodiesel depends on source and type of feedstock. Some payments are limited to a fixed number of litres.

Source: Steenblik, 2007, p. 39.

FIGURE 9
Biofuel production costs in selected countries, 2004 and 2007

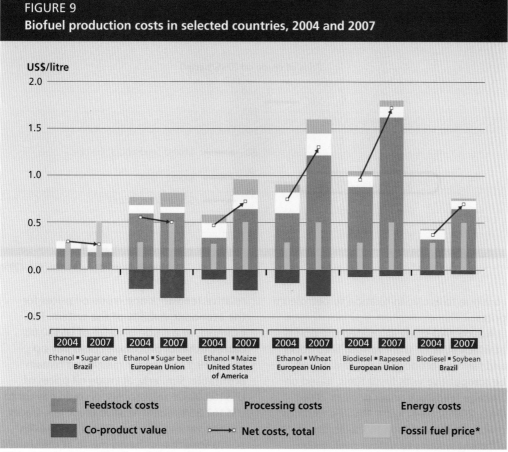

*Net price of petrol or diesel in national markets.

Source: OECD–FAO, 2008.

although with a 25 percent probability of less favourable returns. The maize and wheat projects had very low or negative NPVs and thus would not be economically viable without subsidies. The relatively poor performance of the wheat and maize projects was attributable primarily to higher feedstock costs, which exceeded 75 percent of total production costs.

OECD–FAO (2008) estimated average biofuel production costs in selected countries for alternative feedstocks, shown in Figure 9. Costs are broken down by feedstock, processing and energy costs. The value of co-products is deducted and net costs are indicated in the chart by a square dot. The market price of the nearest equivalent fossil fuel (petrol or diesel) is indicated for each fuel by a green bar.

By far the lowest total costs are for Brazilian sugar-cane ethanol. In all cases for which data are reported, the commodity feedstock accounts for the largest share of total costs. Energy costs for ethanol

production in Brazil are negligible because bagasse, the major co-product of sugar-cane processing, is burned for fuel. In contrast, European and United States processors typically pay for fuel, but sell co-products from the ethanol and biodiesel production processes, usually for animal feed.

After subtracting the value of co-products, the resulting net production costs, on a per litre basis, are also lowest for Brazilian sugar-cane ethanol – the only biofuel that is consistently priced below its fossil-fuel equivalent. Brazilian biodiesel from soybean and United States ethanol from maize have the next lowest net production costs, but in both cases costs exceed the market price of fossil fuels. European biodiesel production costs are more than double those for Brazilian ethanol, reflecting higher feedstock and processing costs. Feedstock costs for maize, wheat, rapeseed and soybean rose sharply between 2004 and 2007, and future profitability will depend on how they

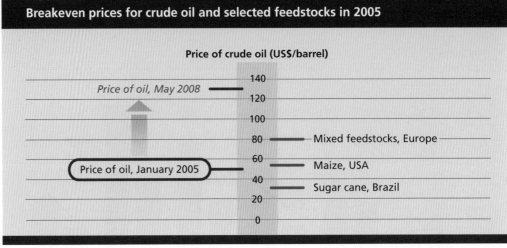

FIGURE 10
Breakeven prices for crude oil and selected feedstocks in 2005

Source: based on data from FAO, 2006a.

continue to evolve in relation to petroleum prices.

A 2006 FAO study calculated the points at which ethanol from various feedstocks and farming production systems would be competitive with fossil fuels, based on average feedstock prices prior to 2006 (FAO, 2006a) (see Figure 10). The findings reveal a wide variation in the ability of different systems to deliver biofuels on an economically competitive basis and are consistent with those of the OECD in that Brazilian sugar cane was found to be competitive at much lower crude oil prices than other feedstocks and production locations. Based on maize prices prior to 2006, United States maize ethanol was found to be competitive at crude oil prices of around US$58/barrel, but it is important to note that this breakeven point will change as feedstock prices change. Indeed, sharp rises in maize prices (partly due to demand for biofuels) and reductions in sugar prices since this analysis was conducted suggest that the competitive advantage of Brazilian sugar-cane ethanol over United States maize ethanol may have widened.

Tyner and Taheripour (2007) took the dynamic nature of commodity prices into account and calculated the breakeven points – without tax credits and incentives – for various combinations of maize-based ethanol and crude oil prices in the United States of America, given existing technologies (Figure 11). Their analysis of a single feedstock reveals the importance of

relative feedstock and crude oil prices for the economic viability of the system. For example, at a crude oil price of US$60.00/barrel, ethanol processors could pay up to US$79.52/tonne for maize and remain profitable. Similarly, at crude oil prices of US$100.00/barrel, processors could pay up to US$162.98/tonne. The solid black line traces out the various parity prices or breakeven points for ethanol-based maize in the United States of America. At price combinations located above and to the left of the parity price line, maize ethanol is profitable; at lower crude oil prices or higher maize prices (combinations below and to the right of the solid line), maize ethanol is not profitable.

Similar analyses could be performed for other feedstocks and production locations. The results would differ according to the technical efficiency of feedstock production and biofuel conversion in the particular setting. The parity price line for lower-cost producers would intersect the vertical axis at a lower point. The slope of the parity price line would depend on the ease with which producers can expand feedstock production and biofuel processing in response to price changes. A country's parity price line could also shift over time in response to technological progress, improvements in infrastructure or institutional innovations.

Tyner and Taheripour (2007) also took into consideration the influence of policy interventions on economic viability. They estimated that the United States renewable fuel standard, tax credits and tariff barriers

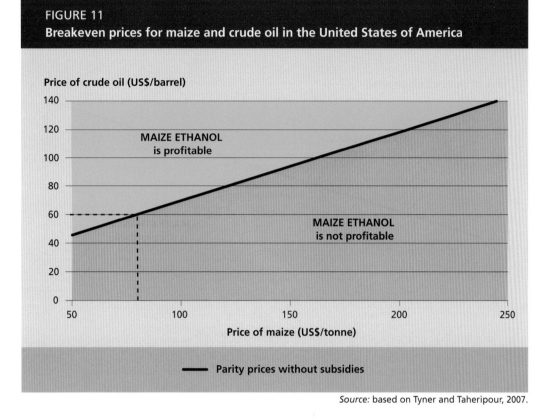

FIGURE 11
Breakeven prices for maize and crude oil in the United States of America

Source: based on Tyner and Taheripour, 2007.

(see Box 4 on United States biofuel policies)
represent a combined subsidy of about
US$1.60/bushel (US$63.00/tonne) for maize
used in ethanol production. Figure 12
shows the breakeven prices for maize at
various crude oil prices, both on the basis
of the energy content of ethanol and also
including the value of the existing subsidies.
The red line takes into account the value
of United States mandates and subsidies
for ethanol. This line is below and to the
right of the black line, indicating that for
a given crude oil price, ethanol processors
can pay a higher price for maize and remain
profitable. The value of the mandates and
subsidies raises the breakeven price for
maize by about US$63.00/tonne for any
given level of petroleum prices. As shown
above, for a crude oil price of US$60/barrel,
maize ethanol would be competitive on an
energy basis as long as the market price for
maize remained below US$79.52/tonne, but
the subsidies enable processors to pay up to
US$142.51/tonne and still remain profitable.

Figure 13 superimposes observed monthly
maize and crude oil prices from June 2003
through April 2008 on top of Tyner and
Taheripour's parity price lines. The data

points show that the relative maize/crude oil
prices generally lie to the right of the black
line, indicating that the maize price is higher
than the breakeven point for ethanol on an
energy basis and that United States maize
ethanol is not competitive with fossil fuels
without subsidies. The price pairs typically
lie between the two lines, indicating that
subsidies are often, but not always, enough
to make maize ethanol competitive.

Looking at the data over time reveals a
stepwise relationship, in which the price of
crude oil seems to pull up maize prices as
ethanol production expands. Before mid-
2004, crude oil prices were so low that maize
could not compete as an ethanol feedstock
even with the available subsidies. Crude oil
prices began to rise in mid-2004, at a time
when maize prices were still quite low. By
early 2005, crude prices had exceeded US$60/
barrel and maize was almost competitive
even without subsidies. The United States
Energy Policy Act of 2005 established the
Renewable Fuel Standard starting at 4 billion
gallons in 2006 and rising to 7.5 billion in
2012. A rush of ethanol plant construction
ensued, and the demand for maize as a
feedstock for ethanol expanded rapidly.

FIGURE 12
Breakeven prices for maize and crude oil with and without subsidies

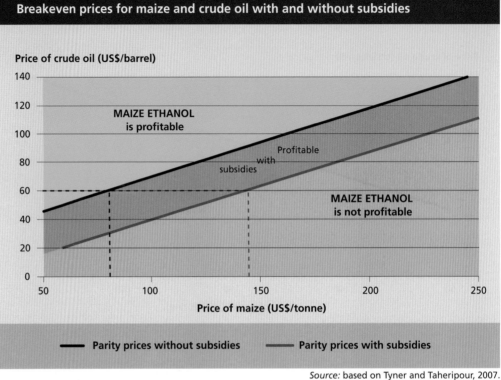

Source: based on Tyner and Taheripour, 2007.

FIGURE 13
Maize and crude oil breakeven prices and observed prices, 2003–08

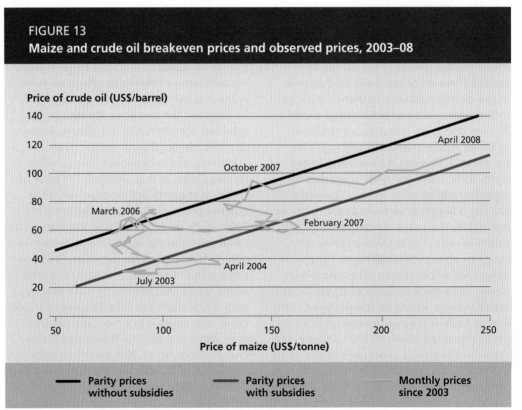

Sources: adapted from Tyner and Taheripour, 2007. Crude oil prices: Brent crude, Chicago Board of Trade (US$/barrel). Maize prices: US Yellow No. 2, Chicago Board of Trade (US$/tonne). Prices downloaded from the Commodity Research Bureau Web site (http://www.crbtrader.com/crbindex/) on 10 June 2008.

The price of maize rose steadily throughout 2006, partly in response to ethanol demand, although other market factors were also involved, while the price of crude oil remained close to US$60/barrel. During this period, the competitiveness of maize as an ethanol feedstock fell sharply even with the subsidies, and many ethanol plants began to operate at a loss. Crude oil prices began rising sharply again in mid-2007, reaching US$135/barrel by mid-2008. Maize thus regained its competitiveness, albeit with subsidies, after mid-2007.[7] Biofuel policies themselves influence the price of agricultural commodities and hence partially determine their competitiveness as feedstocks for biofuel production. The role of policies in shaping biofuel markets is explored more fully in Chapter 4.

The analysis suggests that, given current technology, United States maize ethanol can rarely and only briefly achieve market viability before the price of maize is bid up to the point that it again becomes uncompetitive as a feedstock. Current subsidies and trade barriers offset part of this disadvantage, but do not guarantee competitiveness.

The analysis also illustrates the close link between crude oil prices and prices of agricultural feedstocks. The pattern revealed is consistent with the argument presented at the beginning of this chapter that, because energy markets are large relative to agricultural markets, crude oil prices will drive agricultural prices. It further underlines the role played by government support policies in shaping the relationship between prices in the two sectors.

While similar breakeven point analysis has not been conducted for other biofuel feedstocks and other countries, an examination of the crude oil–commodity price pairs suggests that similar patterns hold for most feedstocks. Figure 14 shows the monthly price pairs for petroleum and rapeseed, palm oil, soybean and sugar. With the exception of sugar, they exhibit the

same general pattern in relation to oil prices as in the case of maize. Sugar prices, in contrast, have been declining in recent years, serving to enhance the profitability of sugar cane as an ethanol feedstock.

Key messages of the chapter

- Liquid biofuels such as bioethanol and biodiesel compete directly with petroleum-based petrol and diesel. Because energy markets are large compared with agricultural markets, energy prices will tend to drive the prices of biofuels and their agricultural feedstocks.
- Biofuel feedstocks also compete with other agricultural crops for productive resources; therefore energy prices will tend to affect prices of all agricultural commodities that rely on the same resource base. For the same reason, producing biofuels from non-food crops will not necessarily eliminate competition between food and fuel.
- For given technologies, the competitiveness of biofuels will depend on the relative prices of agricultural feedstocks and fossil fuels. The relationship will differ among crops, countries, locations and technologies used in biofuel production.
- With the important exception of ethanol produced from sugar cane in Brazil, which has the lowest production costs among the large-scale biofuel-producing countries, biofuels are not generally competitive with fossil fuels without subsidies, even at current high crude oil prices. However, competitiveness can change in line with changes in feedstock and energy prices and developments in technology. Competitiveness is also influenced directly by policies.
- Biofuel development in OECD countries has been promoted and supported by governments through a wide array of policy instruments; a growing number of developing countries are also beginning to introduce policies to promote biofuels. Common policy instruments include mandated blending of biofuels with petroleum-based fuels, subsidies

---

[7] An additional factor stimulating ethanol demand in the United States of America has been the ban in California – effective from January 2004 – on the use of methyl tertiary butyl ether (MBTE). MBTE is a petrol additive used to improve the clean burning of engines, but with suspected adverse impacts on water quality, that can be replaced by ethanol.

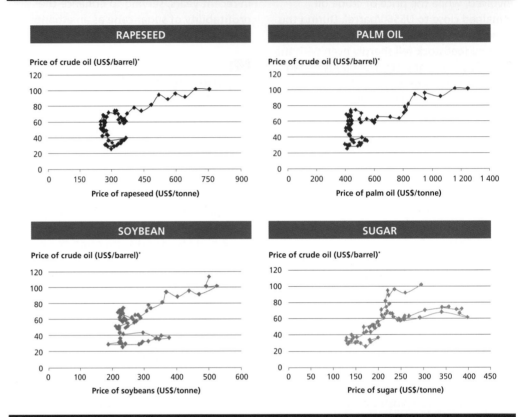

FIGURE 14
Price relationships between crude oil and other biofuel feedstocks, 2003–08

* Monthly prices since 2003.

Sources: Crude oil prices: Brent crude, Chicago Board of Trade (US$ per barrel), downloaded from the Commodity Research Bureau Web site (http://www.crbtrader.com/crbindex/) on 10 June 2008. Commodity prices from FAO international commodity price database.

to production and distribution, and tax incentives. Tariff barriers for biofuels are also widely used to protect domestic producers. These policies have decisively affected the profitability of biofuel production, which in many cases would otherwise not have been commercially viable.

- The main drivers behind government support for the sector have been concerns over climate change and energy security as well as the desire to support the farm sector through increased demand for agricultural products. Although seemingly effective in supporting domestic farmers, the effectiveness of biofuel policies in reaching the climate-change and energy-security objectives is coming under increasing scrutiny.

- In most cases, these policies have been costly and have tended to introduce new distortions to already severely distorted and protected agricultural markets – at the domestic and global levels. This has not tended to favour an efficient international production pattern for biofuels and biofuel feedstocks.

4. Biofuel markets and policy impacts

As discussed in Chapter 3, liquid biofuel development is being driven by a combination of economic and policy factors that are influencing global agriculture – sometimes in unexpected ways. This chapter focuses on biofuel markets and the impact of policies on biofuel and agricultural production and prices. It surveys recent global trends in agricultural commodity markets and examines their links with the expansion of liquid biofuel demand. It then reviews the medium-term outlook for biofuel production and the implications for commodity production and prices, and analyses the potential influence of alternative policy and petroleum price scenarios on how the sector evolves. Finally, it discusses the costs of biofuel policies currently being pursued, as well as some of their market impacts.

Recent biofuel and commodity market developments[8]

Policy support to the production and use of ethanol and biodiesel and the rapid rise in petroleum prices have made biofuels more attractive as substitutes for petroleum-based fuels. Global ethanol production tripled between 2000 and 2007, to reach 62 billion litres (F.O. Licht, 2008, data from the OECD–FAO AgLink-Cosimo database), and the production of biodiesel increased more than ten-fold during the same period, to more than 10 billion litres. Brazil and the United States of America dominate the growth in ethanol production, while the EU has been the major source of growth in biodiesel production. However, many other countries have also begun to increase their output of biofuels.

Agricultural commodity prices have risen sharply over the past three years, driven by a combination of mutually reinforcing factors,

including, among others, the demand for biofuels. The FAO index of nominal food prices has doubled since 2002, and the index of real prices has also risen rapidly. By early 2008, real food prices were 64 percent above the levels of 2002 after four decades of predominantly declining or flat trends. The surge was led by vegetable oil prices, which on average increased by more than 97 percent during the same period, followed by cereals (87 percent), dairy products (58 percent) and rice (46 percent) (Figure 15). Sugar and meat product prices also rose, but not to the same extent.

High-price events, like low-price events, are relatively common occurrences in individual agricultural markets, and indeed some commodity prices had begun to retreat by mid-2008 on the strength of higher predicted harvests (FAO, 2008b). What distinguishes the current state of agricultural markets, however, is the sharp increase in world prices not just of a selected few but, as noted above, nearly all major food and feed commodities and the possibility that the prices may remain high after the effects of short-term shocks dissipate, as predicted in the *OECD-FAO Agricultural Outlook: 2008–2017* (OECD–FAO, 2008). Many factors have contributed to these events, although it is difficult to quantify their relative contributions.

High up in the list of possible factors is the strengthening of linkages among different agricultural commodity markets (i.e. cereals, oilseeds and livestock products) as a result of rapid economic and population growth in many emerging countries. Also prominent is the strengthening of linkages among agricultural commodity markets and those of fossil fuels and biofuels, which influence both production costs and demand for agricultural commodities. Closer linkages with financial markets and the depreciation of the United States dollar against many currencies have also played an important role (FAO, 2008a).

The price boom has also been accompanied by much higher price volatility than in the

---

[8] For more information about current developments in agricultural commodity markets, see FAO (2008a) and the latest issues of *Food Outlook*.

FIGURE 15
Food commodity price trends 1971–2007, with projections to 2017

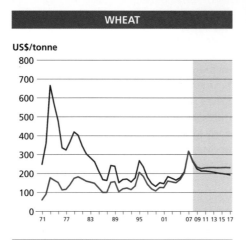

WHEAT

US$/tonne

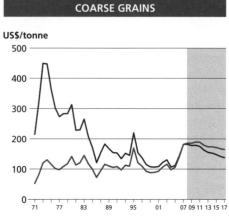

COARSE GRAINS

US$/tonne

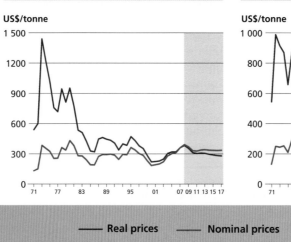

RICE

US$/tonne

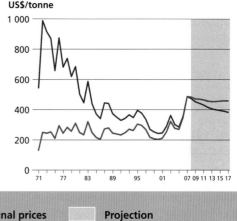

OILSEEDS

US$/tonne

—— Real prices   —— Nominal prices   ▢ Projection

Source: OECD–FAO, 2008.

past, especially in the cereals and oilseeds sectors, highlighting the greater uncertainty in the markets. Yet the current situation differs from the past in that the price volatility has lasted longer – a feature that is as much a result of supply tightness as it is a reflection of changes in the nature of the relationships among agricultural markets for individual commodities, as well as their relationships with others.

A critical trigger for the price hikes has been the decline in cereal production in major exporting countries, which, beginning in 2005 and continuing in 2006, declined annually by 4 and 7 percent respectively. Yields in Australia and Canada fell by about one-fifth in aggregate, and yields were at or below trend in many other countries. The

gradual reduction in cereal stock levels since the mid-1990s is another supply-side factor that has had a significant impact on markets. Indeed, since the previous high-price event in 1995, global stock levels have declined, on average, by 3.4 percent per year as demand growth has outstripped supply. Production shocks at recent low-stock levels helped set the stage for rapid price hikes.

Recent increases in petroleum prices have also raised the costs of producing agricultural commodities; for example, the United States dollar prices of some fertilizers increased by more than 160 percent in the first two months of 2008, compared with the same period in 2007. Indeed, the increase in energy prices has been both rapid and steep, with the Reuters-CRB (Commodity Research

Bureau) energy price index more than tripling since 2003. With freight rates doubling within a one-year period beginning in February 2006, the cost of transporting food to importing countries also has been affected.

Rising petroleum prices have also contributed to a surge in demand for agricultural crops as feedstocks for biofuel production. An estimated 93 million tonnes of wheat and coarse grains were used for ethanol production in 2007, double the level of 2005 (OECD–FAO, 2008). This represents more than half of the total growth in wheat and coarse grain use during the period, but probably accounts for less than half of the increase in prices, as other factors were also involved. Most of this growth can be attributed to the United States of America alone, where the use of maize for ethanol rose to 81 million tonnes in 2007 and is forecast to increase by another 30 percent during the current crop year (FAO, 2008b).

While these recent price trends are clearly a source of concern for low-income consumers, they need to be considered from a longer-term perspective. Figure 15 confirms that although real commodity prices have risen rapidly in recent years, they still remain well below the levels reached in the 1970s and early 1980s. In real terms, coarse grain prices are still lower than the peaks reached in the mid-1990s. While this does not diminish the hardship implied for poor consumers, it does suggest that the current crisis is not without precedent and that policy responses should take into consideration the cyclical nature of commodity markets. Some of the factors underlying the current high prices are transitory in nature and will be mitigated as conditions return to more normal patterns and farmers around the world respond to price incentives. Others factors are of a longer-term, more structural nature, and thus may continue putting upward pressure on prices. Long-term projections suggest that agricultural commodity prices will retreat from their current levels and resume their long-term declining trend in the next few years, although prices for coarse grains and oilseeds are likely to remain above the levels that prevailed during the previous decade (see Part II of this report for a more complete discussion of commodity price determinants and potential future trends).

Even when agricultural commodity prices retreat from the current high levels,

however, demand for biofuels is likely to continue its influence on prices well into the future, as biofuel demand serves to forge closer linkages between the energy and agricultural markets. The influence of energy prices on agricultural commodity prices is not a new phenomenon, given the longstanding reliance on fertilizers and machinery as inputs in commodity production processes. Greater use of agricultural commodities for biofuel production would strengthen this price relationship. Future trends in biofuel production, consumption, trade and prices will depend critically on future developments in the energy markets and, more specifically, on crude oil prices.

Long-term projections for biofuel development

The International Energy Agency (IEA, 2007) foresees a significant expansion of the role of liquid biofuels for transport. Nevertheless, when viewed in the context of both total energy use and total energy use for transport, it will remain relatively limited. Transportation currently accounts for 26 percent of total energy consumption, 94 percent of which is supplied by petroleum and only 0.9 percent by biofuels. As briefly indicated in Chapter 2, in its Reference Scenario in *World Energy Outlook 2007*, the IEA foresees an increase of this share to 2.3 percent in 2015 and 3.2 percent in 2030 (see Table 8). This corresponds to an increase in the total amount of biofuels used in the transport sector, from 19 million Mtoe in 2005 to 57 million in 2015 and 102 million in 2030. The Reference Scenario "is designed to show the outcome, on given assumptions about economic growth, population, energy prices and technology, if nothing more is done by governments to change underlying energy trends. It takes account of those government policies and measures that had already been adopted by mid-2007..." (IEA, 2007, p. 57).

Expansion of biofuel production and consumption could be stronger, depending on policies adopted. Under the IEA's Alternative Policy Scenario, which "takes into account those policies and measures that countries are currently considering and are assumed to adopt and implement" (IEA, 2007, p. 66), the share is projected

TABLE 8
Energy demand by source and sector: reference scenario

	ENERGY DEMAND (Mtoe)						SHARE (Percentage)		
	1980	1990	2000	2005	2015	2030	2005	2015	2030
Total primary energy supply by SOURCE	7 228	8 755	10 023	11 429	14 361	17 721	100	100	100
Coal	1 786	2 216	2 292	2 892	3 988	4 994	25	28	28
Oil	3 106	3 216	3 647	4 000	4 720	5 585	35	33	32
Gas	1 237	1 676	2 089	2 354	3 044	3 948	21	21	22
Nuclear	186	525	675	714	804	854	6	6	5
Hydro	147	184	226	251	327	416	2	2	2
Biomass and waste	753	903	1 041	1 149	1 334	1 615	10	9	9
Other renewable	12	35	53	61	145	308	1	1	2
Total energy consumption by SECTOR	..	6 184	..	7 737	9 657	11 861	100	100	100
Residential, services and agriculture	..	2 516	..	2 892	3 423	4 122	37	35	35
Industry	..	2 197	..	2 834	3 765	4 576	37	39	39
Transport	..	1 471	..	2 011	2 469	3 163	26	26	27
Oil	..	*1 378*	..	*1 895*	*2 296*	*2 919*	*94*	*93*	*92*
Biofuels	..	*6*	..	*19*	*57*	*102*	*1*	*2*	*3*
Other fuels	..	*87*	..	*96*	*117*	*142*	*5*	*5*	*4*

Note: .. = not available. Data presented are subject to rounding.
Source: IEA, 2007.

to increase to 3.3 percent in 2015 and 5.9 percent in 2030, corresponding to an increase in total volume to 78 Mtoe in 2015 and 164 Mtoe in 2030.

Recent and projected increases in biofuel feedstock production are substantial in relation to current agricultural production. Production increases can be achieved by extending the area devoted to producing biofuel feedstocks – either via shifts from production of other crops on land already in cultivation, or by converting land not already in crop production, such as grassland or forest land. Alternatively, production can be increased by improving the yields of biofuel feedstocks on land already in production.

To achieve their long-term biofuel production scenarios, the IEA projects an increase in the share of cropland devoted to biofuel feedstocks from 1 percent in 2004 to 2.5 percent by 2030 under the Reference Scenario, 3.8 percent under the Alternative Policy Scenario and 4.2 percent

under a scenario where second-generation technologies become available (Table 9) (IEA, 2006, pp. 414–416). Land used directly for biofuel production under these various scenarios would increase to between 11.6 and 15.7 percent of cropland in the EU and 5.4 and 10.2 percent in the United States of America and Canada, but would remain below 3.4 percent in other regions (although it could be higher in individual countries, such as Brazil). The environmental implications of area expansion *vis-à-vis* intensification are discussed further in Chapter 5.

Medium-term outlook for biofuels[9]

The *OECD-FAO Agricultural Outlook 2008–2017* includes a full set of projections for

---

[9] The analysis in this section is based on OECD–FAO (2008). Permission to use this material is gratefully acknowledged.

TABLE 9
Land requirements for biofuel production

COUNTRY GROUPING	2004		2030					
			Reference scenario		Alternative policy scenario		Second-generation biofuels case	
	(Million ha)	(Percentage of arable land)	(Million ha)	(Percentage of arable land)	(Million ha)	(Percentage of arable land)	(Million ha)	(Percentage of arable land)
Africa and Near East	–	–	0.8	0.3	0.9	0.3	1.1	0.4
Developing Asia	–	–	5.0	1.2	10.2	2.5	11.8	2.8
European Union	2.6	1.2	12.6	11.6	15.7	14.5	17.1	15.7
Latin America	2.7	0.9	3.5	2.4	4.3	2.9	5.0	3.4
OECD Pacific	–	–	0.3	0.7	1.0	2.1	1.0	2.0
Transition economies	–	–	0.1	0.1	0.2	0.1	0.2	0.1
United States of America and Canada	8.4	1.9	12.0	5.4	20.4	9.2	22.6	10.2
World	13.8	1.0	34.5	2.5	52.8	3.8	58.5	4.2

Note: – = negligible.
Sources: FAO, 2008a; IEA, 2006.

future supply, demand, trade and prices for ethanol and biodiesel, which are summarized in this section. The projections are based on a linked model of 58 countries and regions and 20 agricultural commodities. The model includes ethanol and biodiesel markets for 17 countries. It allows an integrated analysis of energy and agricultural markets and supports the analysis of alternative policy scenarios. The baseline projections reflect government policies in place as of early 2008 and are based on a consistent set of assumptions regarding exogenous factors such as population, economic growth, currency exchange rates and global petroleum prices.

The outlook for ethanol

Figure 16 shows the OECD/FAO baseline projections for global ethanol production, trade and prices. Production is projected to more than double by 2017, reaching 127 billion litres compared with 62 billion litres in 2007. Both figures include ethanol produced for uses other than fuel, whereas the 52 billion litres reported in Table 1 (page 15) included only biofuel ethanol. According to the projections, global ethanol prices should rise during the early years of the projection period before retreating to levels around US$51 per hectolitre, as

production capacity expands. As a result of increases in mandated blending of transport fuels in OECD countries, international trade in ethanol is expected to grow to almost 11 billion litres, most of it originating in Brazil. However, traded ethanol will continue to account for only a small share of total production.

Brazil and the United States of America will retain their positions as the largest ethanol producers through to 2017, as shown in Figure 17, but many other countries are expanding production rapidly. In the United States of America, ethanol production is expected to double during the projection period, reaching some 52 billion litres by 2017, corresponding to 42 percent of global production. Total use is projected to increase more rapidly than production, and net imports are expected to grow to about 9 percent of domestic ethanol use by 2017. Ethanol production in Brazil is also expected to continue its rapid growth, reaching 32 billion litres by 2017. With sugar cane remaining the cheapest of the main ethanol feedstocks, Brazil will remain highly competitive and is expected to almost triple its ethanol exports to 8.8 billion litres by 2017. By that year, 85 percent of global ethanol exports are projected to originate from Brazil.

BOX 6
Main sources of uncertainty for biofuel projections

The projections presented in this section give some indication of the possible future direction of world biofuel production, trade and prices. However, it is important to emphasize that the projections are subject to a number of uncertainties. Most importantly, they assume that basic agricultural commodities will continue to represent the bulk of feedstocks for ethanol and biodiesel throughout the next decade and that the technical and economic constraints that currently limit the production and marketing of biofuels based on other feedstocks will remain prohibitive. In particular, it is assumed that second-generation ethanol produced from cellulose and biomass-based diesel fuels will not become economically viable on any meaningful scale during the projection period.

However, numerous countries are engaged in research aimed at overcoming existing constraints and, although prospects for success remain uncertain, it is not impossible that the first commercial production plants for second-generation biofuels could become operational during the next decade. This would significantly change the relationship between biofuel production and agricultural markets, especially with regard to the extent that feedstocks for these fuels would come from either crop residues or energy crops grown on land not suitable for food production.

Other uncertainties relate to future developments in the markets for fossil energy and agriculture. Feedstock prices represent a large share of total biofuel production costs and have a significant impact on the economic viability of the sector. Prices for coarse grains and vegetable oils are projected to remain at relatively high levels (when expressed in United States dollars) compared with the past, despite some decline in the short run, while sugar prices should increase after 2008. Production costs for most biofuels are thus likely to remain a significant constraint over the projection period. The baseline projections assume that petroleum prices will increase slowly throughout the projection period, from US$90/barrel in 2008 to US$104/barrel by 2017. These price assumptions are a major source of uncertainty for the projections; for example, the previous OECD–FAO baseline assumed that petroleum prices would remain in the range of US$50–55 during the 2007–16 projection period (OECD–FAO, 2007), while actual petroleum prices exceeded US$129/barrel in May 2008.

Finally, it must be borne in mind that, in most countries, biofuel production remains heavily dependent on public-support policies and border protection, as discussed in Chapter 3. The debate on the potential and actual benefits that derive from supporting biofuel production and use continues. Support schemes are developing rapidly and their future course is impossible to predict. Recent policy changes that are not accounted for in the projections include the new United States Energy Act signed into law in December 2007 and the 2007 Farm Bill approved by Congress in May 2008 (see Box 4 on pp. 30–31).

In the EU, total ethanol production is projected to reach 12 billion litres by 2017. As this is still well below the projected consumption of 15 billion litres, net ethanol imports are expected to reach around 3 billion litres. A strong increase in blending obligations, which can only partially be met by EU production, will be the main driver behind EU ethanol imports.

Ethanol production in several other countries is projected to grow rapidly, led by China, India, Thailand and several African countries. China is projected to more than double its consumption by 2017, which will exceed domestic production. Strong production growth is forecast for India and Thailand. The Indian Government is supporting the development of an ethanol industry based on sugar cane. Production is thus set to increase to 3.6 billion litres by 2017, while consumption is projected to reach 3.2 billion litres. In Thailand, production is

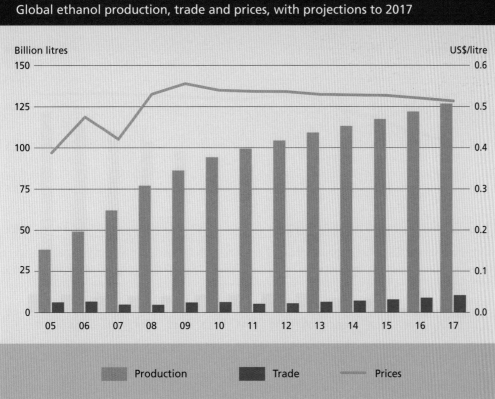

FIGURE 16
Global ethanol production, trade and prices, with projections to 2017

Source: OECD–FAO, 2008.

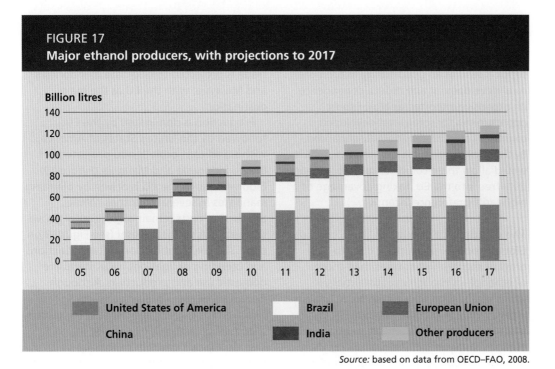

FIGURE 17
Major ethanol producers, with projections to 2017

Source: based on data from OECD–FAO, 2008.

projected to reach 1.8 billion litres by 2017, while consumption is projected at 1.5 billion litres. Growth in production and consumption is underpinned by the government objective of reducing reliance on imported oil. Thus, the energy share of ethanol in petrol-type fuel use is assumed to increase from 2 percent to 12 percent between 2008 and 2017.

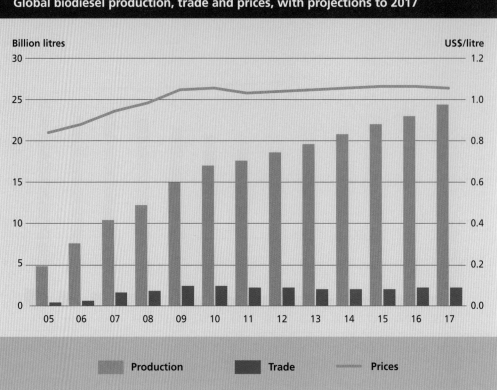

FIGURE 18
Global biodiesel production, trade and prices, with projections to 2017

Production ◼ Trade ◼ Prices ▬

Source: OECD–FAO, 2008.

Many African countries are beginning to invest in the development of ethanol production. Developing a biofuels/bioenergy sector is seen as an opportunity to promote rural development and reduce dependence on expensive imported energy. Export opportunities for some least-developed countries could be considerably enhanced by the Everything But Arms initiative, which would allow these countries to export ethanol duty-free into the EU, taking advantage of a high tariff-preference incentive.

The outlook for biodiesel

Global biodiesel production is set to grow at slightly higher rates than those of ethanol – although at substantially lower levels – and to reach some 24 billion litres by 2017 (Figure 18). Mandates and tax concessions in several countries, predominantly in the EU, are driving the growth in biodiesel projections. World biodiesel prices are expected to remain well above the production costs of fossil diesel, in the range of US$104–106 per hectolitre, for most of the projection period. Total

trade in biodiesel is expected to grow in the early years of the projection period but change little in following years. Most of the trade is projected to originate in Indonesia and Malaysia, with the EU as the main destination.

Production is dominated by the EU, followed by the United States of America, with significant growth also projected for Brazil, Indonesia and Malaysia (Figure 19). Biodiesel use in the EU is driven by blending mandates in several countries. While production costs remain significantly above the net costs of fossil diesel (see Figure 9 on page 35), the combination of tax reductions and blending obligations helps stimulate domestic use and production. Although EU biodiesel use is projected to decline in relative terms, it will still account for more than half of global biodiesel use in 2017. This strong demand will be met by both increased domestic production and growing imports. Production margins are projected to improve considerably compared with those of the very difficult year 2007, but to remain tight.

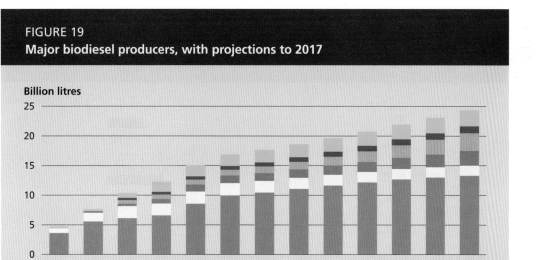

FIGURE 19
Major biodiesel producers, with projections to 2017

Source: based on data from OECD–FAO, 2008.

Biodiesel use in the United States of America, which tripled in both 2005 and 2006, is projected to remain largely unchanged throughout the projection period, as biodiesel remains expensive compared with fossil diesel. Biodiesel production in Brazil, which began in 2006, is projected to expand rapidly in the short term in response to increased biodiesel prices and hence improved production margins. In the longer run, however, production expansion should slow down and remain limited to supplying domestic demand, which is projected to grow to some 2.6 billion litres by 2017.

Indonesia is expected to emerge as a major player on the biodiesel market. The Indonesian Government reduced and then eliminated price subsidies on fossil fuels in 2005, allowing the biofuel industry to become economically viable. Biodiesel production on a commercial scale started in 2006 and had expanded to an annual production of about 600 million litres by 2007. Fuelled by domestic palm-oil production, the industry enjoys a competitive advantage, which will propel Indonesia towards becoming the second-largest producer in the world, with annual production rising steadily to reach 3 billion litres by 2017. Based on the consumption targets established by the government,

domestic demand is expected to develop in parallel with production.

Malaysia is the second largest palm-oil producer in the world, which also places the country in a prime position to play a major role in the world biodiesel market. Commercial biodiesel production began in 2006 and grew to an annual production of about 360 million litres by 2007. Steadily expanding domestic palm-oil production will provide the basis for a rapid growth of the biofuel industry during the coming decade. Production is projected to increase at a rate of about 10 percent annually, reaching 1.1 billion litres by 2017. In the absence of consumption mandates, domestic use is not expected to increase significantly. The industry will be predominantly export-oriented, with the EU as its target market.

In some African countries and in India there has also been some investment directed towards stimulating biodiesel production from *Jatropha curcas* on marginal lands. High biodiesel prices and an interest in developing the rural economy and reducing dependence on imported oil, which is costly to transport to interior locations with poor infrastructure, lay behind these investments. It is extremely difficult to establish projections for jatropha-based production, as experience with commercial production of this crop is limited. In this projection, preliminary estimates

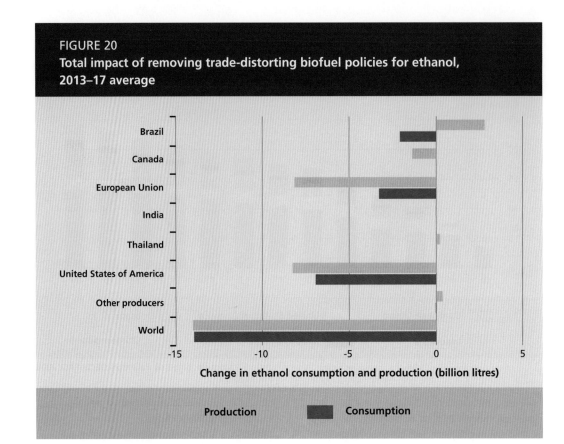

FIGURE 20
Total impact of removing trade-distorting biofuel policies for ethanol, 2013–17 average

Change in ethanol consumption and production (billion litres)

Production   Consumption

Source: FAO, 2008c.

were made for Ethiopia, India, Mozambique and the United Republic of Tanzania, which indicate a total production of between 60 000 and 95 000 tonnes in each of these countries. For African countries, it is assumed that all biodiesel production will come from jatropha seed.

Impacts of biofuel policies

The joint OECD-FAO AgLink-Cosimo modelling framework was used to analyse alternative policy scenarios for biofuels (FAO, 2008c). As discussed in Chapter 3, countries use a range of policy instruments to support the production and consumption of biofuels. The policy scenario reported here simulates the effects of removing domestic subsidies (tax concessions, tax credits and direct support for the production of biofuels) and trade restrictions in OECD and non-OECD countries, while retaining mandatory blending and use requirements.

This scenario broadly mimics the "full liberalization" scenarios that are frequently conducted for agriculture in which trade

restrictions and trade-distorting domestic subsidies are eliminated but non-trade-distorting policies such as environmental measures are allowed to remain. Any number of scenarios could be defined, and it should be emphasized that the results are highly dependent on the precise scenario and model specification. As such, they should be taken as broadly suggestive – not precisely predictive – of the effects of removing existing subsidies and trade barriers. The 2007 United States Energy Independence and Security Act and the proposed new EU Bioenergy Directive are not considered in this scenario.

Figure 20 summarizes the total impacts on ethanol production and consumption that would result from the removal of all trade-distorting biofuel policies in OECD and other countries. The removal of tariffs and subsidies would lead to a decline in global ethanol production and consumption, of about 10–15 percent. The largest reductions would occur in the EU, where ethanol support measured in per litre terms is very high (see Chapter 3), and in the United States of America, the largest ethanol producer.

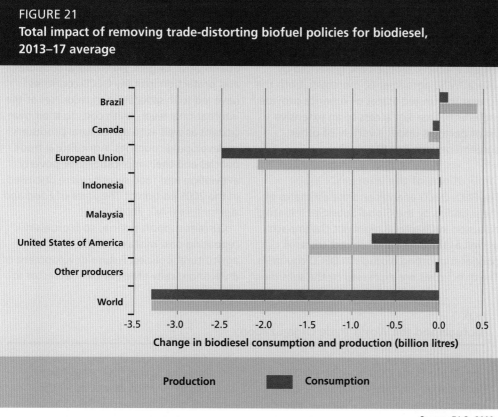

FIGURE 21

Total impact of removing trade-distorting biofuel policies for biodiesel, 2013–17 average

Change in biodiesel consumption and production (billion litres)

Production   Consumption

Source: FAO, 2008c.

Consumption in both would also fall, but by a lesser amount because mandated use targets would remain in place. Imports would increase significantly in currently protected markets, while production and exports from Brazil and some other developing-country suppliers would increase.

Figure 21 summarizes the results of the same scenario but for biodiesel. At the global level, the impacts of removing trade barriers and trade-distorting domestic support would be somewhat larger in percentage terms than for ethanol, with reductions in production and consumption of around 15–20 percent. Most countries would see major declines because the industry currently depends heavily on subsidies to achieve competitiveness with petroleum-based diesel.

The elimination of current biofuel trade-distorting policies would have implications for ethanol and biodiesel prices and for agricultural commodity prices and output. Global ethanol prices would increase about 10 percent because production in several heavily subsidized countries would decline more than consumption, thereby increasing

the demand for exports. Global biodiesel prices, in contrast, would fall slightly as the reduction in EU consumption would translate into a decline in import demand. Agricultural commodity feedstock prices would also be affected by the elimination of biofuel subsidies. Vegetable oil and maize prices would decline by about 5 percent and sugar prices would rise slightly compared with the baseline. Global crop area devoted to the production of coarse grains and wheat would decline slightly, by about 1 percent, while sugar-cane area would increase by about 1 percent.

Historically, biomass and biofuel trade flows have been small, as most production has been destined for domestic consumption. However, in the coming years, international trade in biofuels and feedstocks may escalate rapidly to satisfy increasing worldwide demand. Policies that liberalize or constrict the trade of biofuel products are likely to have a strong impact on future production and consumption patterns, and international trade rules will thus assume critical importance for biofuel development internationally (see Box 7).

Many countries impose tariffs on biofuel imports, as discussed in Chapter 3, with the EU and the United States of America being the most important because theirs are the largest markets. Biofuels are governed by several WTO agreements; moreover, both the EU and the United States of America provide preferential market access to an extensive list of partners under a variety of other agreements (see Box 8).

Implications of the analysis

The FAO–OECD analysis and the estimates of the subsidies by the Global Subsidies Initiative discussed in Chapter 3 highlight the impacts, as well as the direct and indirect costs, of policies supporting biofuels in OECD countries. The direct costs are expressed by the subsidies, which are borne either by taxpayers or by consumers. The indirect costs derive from the distorted resource allocation resulting from selective support to biofuels and mandated quantitative targets. Agricultural subsidies and protection in many OECD countries have led to misallocation of resources at the international level – with costs to their own citizens as well as to agricultural producers in developing countries. Agricultural trade policies and their implications for poverty alleviation and food security were discussed in the 2005 edition of *The State of Food and Agriculture* (FAO, 2005).

Current support policies to biofuels risk repeating past mistakes in the field of agricultural policies. Future development of an economically efficient biofuel sector at

---

BOX 7
Biofuels and the World Trade Organization

The World Trade Organization (WTO) does not currently have a trade regime specific to biofuels. International trade in biofuels falls, therefore, under the rules of the General Agreement on Tariffs and Trade (GATT 1994), which covers trade in all goods, as well as other relevant WTO Agreements such as the Agreement on Agriculture, the Agreement on Technical Barriers to Trade, the Agreement on the Application of Sanitary and Phytosanitary Measures and the Agreement on Subsidies and Countervailing Measures. Agricultural products are subject to the GATT and to the general rules of the WTO insofar as the Agreement on Agriculture does not contain derogating provisions.

Key trade-related issues include the classification for tariff purposes of biofuel products as agricultural, industrial or environmental goods; the role of subsidies in increasing production; and the degree of consistency among various domestic measures and WTO standards.

The Agreement on Agriculture (AoA) covers products from Chapters 1 to 24 of the Harmonized System, with the exception of fish and fish products and the addition of a number of specific products, such as hides and skins, silk, wool, cotton, flax and modified starches.

The discipline of the AoA is based on three pillars: market access, domestic subsidies and export subsidies. One of the main features of the AoA is that it allows Members to pay subsidies in derogation from the Agreement on Subsidies and Countervailing Measures.

The Harmonized System classification affects how products are characterized under specific WTO Agreements. For example, ethanol is considered an agricultural product and is therefore subject to Annex 1 of the WTO AoA. Biodiesel, on the other hand, is considered an industrial product and is therefore not subject to the disciplines of the AoA. Paragraph 31(iii) of the Doha Development Agenda has launched negotiations on "the reduction or, as appropriate, elimination of tariff and non-tariff barriers to environmental goods and services". Some WTO Members have suggested that renewable energy products, including ethanol and biodiesel, should be classified as "environmental goods" and therefore subject to negotiations under the "Environmental Goods and Services" cluster.

Source: based on FAO, 2007b and GBEP, 2007.

the international level will depend on the establishment of appropriate non-distorting national policies as well as trade rules that encourage an efficient geographic pattern of biofuel production.

In addition to being costly, current biofuel policies may have unintended consequences, especially to the extent that they promote excessively rapid growth in biofuel production from an already stressed natural resource base. Some of these consequences of rapid policy-induced biofuel development are examined further in the following two chapters: Chapter 5 discusses the environmental impacts of biofuels, while the socio-economic and food-security impacts are the focus of Chapter 6.

Key messages of the chapter

- Growing demand for liquid biofuels is only one of several factors underlying the recent sharp increases in agricultural commodity prices. The exact contribution of expanding biofuel demand to these price increases is difficult to quantify. However, biofuel demand will continue to exercise upward pressure on agricultural prices for considerable time to come.
- Biofuel demand and supply are expected to continue to increase rapidly, but the share of liquid biofuels in overall transport fuel supply will remain limited.

BOX 8
Biofuels and preferential trade initiatives

For developing countries, the challenges associated with producing bioenergy for the international market are particularly acute. Trade opportunities may be reduced by measures that focus exclusively on enhancing production in developed countries, or by protectionist measures designed to limit market access. Tariff escalation on biofuels in developed-country markets can restrict developing countries to exporting feedstocks, such as unprocessed molasses and crude oils, while the actual conversion into biofuels – with its associated value-added – often occurs elsewhere.

A number of European Union (EU) and United States preferential trade initiatives and agreements have been introduced that offer new opportunities for some developing countries to benefit from the increasing global demand for bioenergy. Preferential trade with the EU for developing countries falls under the EU's Generalised System of Preferences (GSP). In addition, the Everything But Arms (EBA) initiative and the Cotonou Agreement contain provisions of relevance to the bioenergy sector. Under the current GSP, in effect until 31 December 2008, duty-free access to the EU is provided to denatured and undenatured alcohol. The GSP also has an incentive programme for ethanol

producers and exporters who adhere to sustainable development principles and good governance. The EBA initiative provides least-developed countries with duty-free and quota-free access to ethanol exports, while the Cotonou Agreement provides duty-free access for certain imports from African, Caribbean and Pacific countries. The Euro-Mediterranean Association Agreements also contain provisions for preferential trade in biofuels for certain countries in the Near East and North Africa. In the United States of America, ethanol may be imported duty-free from certain Caribbean countries under the Caribbean Basin Initiative, although there are specific quantitative and qualitative restrictions depending on the country of origin of the feedstocks. Provisions for duty-free ethanol imports have also been proposed in the US-Central America Free Trade Agreement negotiations.

However, while such preferential access can provide opportunities for beneficiaries, it also creates problems of trade diversion, to the disadvantage of the developing countries not benefiting from the preferential access.

Source: based on FAO, 2007b.

However, the projections are surrounded by a high degree of uncertainty mainly because of uncertainties concerning fossil fuel prices, biofuel policies and technology developments.

- Brazil, the EU and the United States of America are expected to remain the largest producers of liquid biofuels, but production is also projected to expand in a number of developing countries.
- Biofuel policies have significant implications for international markets, trade and prices for biofuels and agricultural commodities. Current trends in biofuel production, consumption and trade, as well as the global outlook, are strongly influenced by existing policies, especially those implemented in the EU and United States of America, which promote biofuel production and consumption while protecting domestic producers.

- The biofuel policies of OECD countries impose large costs on their own taxpayers and consumers and create unintended consequences.
- Trade policies *vis-à-vis* biofuels discriminate against developing-country producers of biofuel feedstocks and impede the emergence of biofuel processing and exporting sectors in developing countries.
- Many current biofuel policies distort biofuel and agricultural markets and influence the location and development of the global industry, such that production may not occur in the most economically or environmentally suitable locations.
- International policy disciplines for biofuels are needed to prevent a repeat of the kind of global policy failure that exists in the agriculture sector.

5. Environmental impacts of biofuels

Although biofuel production remains small in the context of total energy demand, it is significant in relation to current levels of agricultural production. The potential environmental and social implications of its continued growth must be recognized. For example, reduced greenhouse gas emissions are among the explicit goals of some policy measures to support biofuel production. Unintended negative impacts on land, water and biodiversity count among the side-effects of agricultural production in general, but they are of particular concern with respect to biofuels. The extent of such impacts depends on how biofuel feedstocks are produced and processed, the scale of production and, in particular, how they influence land-use change, intensification and international trade. This chapter reviews the environmental implications of biofuels; the social implications will be considered in the following chapter.

Will biofuels help mitigate climate change?[10]

Until recently, many policy-makers assumed that the replacement of fossil fuels with fuels generated from biomass would have significant and positive climate-change effects by generating lower levels of the greenhouse gases that contribute to global warming. Bioenergy crops can reduce or offset greenhouse gas emissions by directly removing carbon dioxide from the air as they grow and storing it in crop biomass and soil. In addition to biofuels, many of these crops generate co-products such as protein for animal feed, thus saving on energy that would have been used to make feed by other means.

Despite these potential benefits, however, scientific studies have revealed that different biofuels vary widely in their greenhouse gas balances when compared with petrol.

Depending on the methods used to produce the feedstock and process the fuel, some crops can even generate more greenhouse gases than do fossil fuels. For example, nitrous oxide, a greenhouse gas with a global-warming potential around 300 times greater than that of carbon dioxide, is released from nitrogen fertilizers. Moreover, greenhouse gases are emitted at other stages in the production of bioenergy crops and biofuels: in producing the fertilizers, pesticides and fuel used in farming, during chemical processing, transport and distribution, up to final use.

Greenhouse gases can also be emitted by direct or indirect land-use changes triggered by increased biofuel production, for example when carbon stored in forests or grasslands is released from the soil during land conversion to crop production. For example, while maize produced for ethanol can generate greenhouse gas savings of about 1.8 tonnes of carbon dioxide per hectare per year, and switchgrass – a possible second-generation crop – can generate savings of 8.6 tonnes per hectare per year, the conversion of grassland to produce those crops can release 300 tonnes per hectare, and conversion of forest land can release 600–1 000 tonnes per hectare (Fargione et al., 2008; The Royal Society, 2008; Searchinger, 2008).

Life-cycle analysis is the analytical tool used to calculate greenhouse gas balances. The greenhouse gas balance is the result of a comparison between all emissions of greenhouse gases throughout the production phases and use of a biofuel and all the greenhouse gases emitted in producing and using the equivalent energy amount of the respective fossil fuel. This well-established, but complex, method systematically analyses each component of the value chain to estimate greenhouse gas emissions (Figure 22).

The starting point in estimating the greenhouse gas balance is a well-defined set of boundaries for a specific biofuel system, which is compared with a suitable

---

"conventional" reference system – in most cases petrol. Several biofuel feedstocks also generate co-products, such as press cake or livestock feed. These are considered "avoided" greenhouse gas emissions and are assessed by comparing them with similar stand-alone products or by allocation (e.g. by energy content or market price). Greenhouse gas balances differ widely among crops and locations, depending on feedstock production methods, conversion technologies and use. Inputs such as nitrogen fertilizer and the type of electricity generation (e.g. from coal or oil, or nuclear) used to convert feedstocks to biofuels may result in widely varying levels of greenhouse gas emissions and also differ from one region to another.

Most life-cycle analyses of biofuels, to date, have been undertaken for cereal and oilseeds in the EU and the United States of America and for sugar-cane ethanol in Brazil.

A limited number of studies have considered vegetable oil; biodiesel from palm oil, cassava and jatropha; and biomethane from biogas. Given the wide range of biofuels, feedstocks and production and conversion technologies, we would expect a similarly wide range of outcomes in terms of emission reductions – which is indeed the case. Most studies have found that producing first-generation biofuels from current feedstocks results in emission reductions in the range of 20–60 percent relative to fossil fuels, provided the most efficient systems are used and carbon releases deriving from land-use change are excluded. Figure 23 shows estimated ranges of reduction in greenhouse gas emissions for a series of crops and locations, excluding the effects of land-use change. Brazil, which has long experience of producing ethanol from sugar cane, shows even greater reductions. Second-generation biofuels, although still

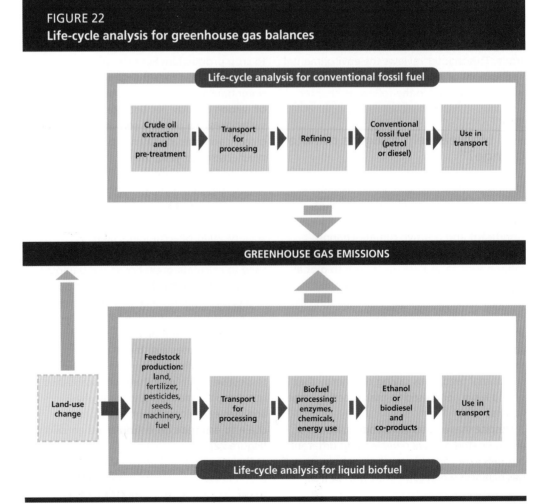

FIGURE 22
Life-cycle analysis for greenhouse gas balances

Source: FAO.

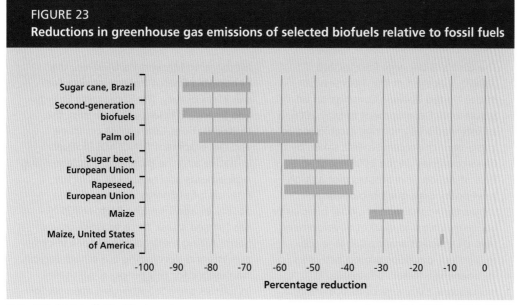

FIGURE 23
Reductions in greenhouse gas emissions of selected biofuels relative to fossil fuels

Note: Excludes the effects of land-use change.

Sources: IEA, 2006, and FAO, 2008d.

insignificant at the commercial level, typically offer emission reductions in the order of 70–90 percent, compared with fossil diesel and petrol, also excluding carbon releases related to land-use change.

Several recent studies have found that the most marked differences in results stem from allocation methods chosen for co-products, assumptions on nitrous oxide emissions and land-use-related carbon emission changes. At present, a number of different methods are being used to conduct life-cycle analysis and, as noted above, some of these do not consider the complex topic of land-use change. The parameters measured and the quality of the data used in the assessment need to comply with set standards. Efforts are under way within, among others, the Global Bioenergy Partnership, to develop a harmonized methodology for assessing greenhouse gas balances. There is a similar need for harmonization in assessing the broader environmental and social impacts of bioenergy crops to ensure that results are transparent and consistent across a wide range of systems.

In assessing greenhouse gas balances, the data on emissions emanating from land-use change are crucial if the resulting picture is to be complete and accurate. Such emissions will occur early in the biofuel production cycle and, if sufficiently large, may require many years before they are compensated by emissions savings obtained

in subsequent stages of production and use. When land-use changes are included in the analysis, greenhouse gas emissions for some biofuel feedstocks and production systems may be even higher than those for fossil fuels. Fargione *et al.* (2008) estimated that the conversion of rainforests, peatlands, savannahs or grasslands to produce ethanol and biodiesel in Brazil, Indonesia, Malaysia or the United States of America releases at least 17 times as much carbon dioxide as those biofuels save annually by replacing fossil fuels. They find that this "carbon debt" would take 48 years to repay in the case of Conservation Reserve Program land returned to maize ethanol production in the United States of America, over 300 years to repay if Amazonian rainforest is converted for soybean biodiesel production, and over 400 years to repay if tropical peatland rainforest is converted for palm-oil biodiesel production in Indonesia or Malaysia.

Righelato and Spracklen (2007) estimated the carbon emissions avoided by various ethanol and biodiesel feedstocks grown on existing cropland (i.e. sugar cane, maize, wheat and sugar beet for ethanol, and rapeseed and woody biomass for diesel). They found that, in each case, more carbon would be sequestered over a 30-year period by converting the cropland to forest. They argue that if the objective of biofuel support policies is to mitigate global warming, then fuel efficiency and forest conservation

BOX 9
The Global Bioenergy Partnership

The Global Bioenergy Partnership (GBEP), launched at the 14th session of the United Nations Commission on Sustainable Development in May 2006, is an international initiative established to implement the commitments taken by the G8+5 countries[1] in the 2005 Gleneagles Plan of Action. It promotes global high-level policy dialogue on bioenergy; supports national and regional bioenergy policy-making and market development; favours efficient and sustainable uses of biomass; develops project activities in bioenergy; fosters bilateral and multilateral exchange of information, skills and technology; and facilitates bioenergy integration into energy markets by tackling specific barriers in the supply chain.

The Partnership is chaired by Italy, and FAO is a Partner and hosts the GBEP Secretariat. GBEP cooperates with FAO's International Bioenergy Platform, the International Biofuels Forum, the International Partnership for the Hydrogen Economy, the Mediterranean Renewable Energy Programme, the

Methane to Markets Partnership, the Renewable Energy Policy Network for the 21st Century, the Renewable Energy and Energy Efficiency Partnership, the United Nations Conference on Trade and Development (UNCTAD) BioFuels Initiative and the Bioenergy Implementing Agreements and related tasks of the International Energy Agency, among others. In addition, the Partnership has formed a task force to work on harmonizing methodologies for life-cycle analysis and developing a methodological framework for this purpose. All these initiatives provide important avenues for assisting both developing and developed countries in building national regulatory frameworks for bioenergy.

---

[1] The G8+5 group comprises the G8 countries (Canada, France, Germany, Italy, Japan, the Russian Federation, the United Kingdom and the United States of America), plus the five major emerging economies (Brazil, China, India, Mexico and South Africa).

and restoration would be more effective alternatives.

Among the options for reducing greenhouse gas emissions that are currently being discussed, biofuels are one important alternative – but in many cases improving energy efficiency and conservation, increasing carbon sequestration through reforestation or changes in agricultural practices, or using other forms of renewable energy can be more cost-effective. For example, in the United States of America, improving average vehicle-fuel efficiency by one mile per gallon may reduce greenhouse gas emissions as much as all current United States ethanol production from maize (Tollefson, 2008). Doornbosch and Steenblik (2007) estimated that reducing greenhouse gas emissions via biofuels costs over US$500 in terms of subsidies per tonne of carbon dioxide in the United States of America (maize-based ethanol) and the cost can

be as high as US$4 520 in the EU (ethanol from sugar beet and maize) – much higher than the market price of carbon dioxide-equivalent offsets. Enkvist, Naucler and Rosander (2007) report that relatively straightforward measures to reduce energy consumption, such as better insulation of new buildings or increased efficiency of heating and air-conditioning systems, have carbon dioxide abatement costs of less than €40 per tonne.

Both the scientific and policy dimensions of sustainable bioenergy development are evolving rapidly (almost on a weekly basis). A comprehensive understanding of the relevant issues, including land-use change, and proper assessment of greenhouse gas balances are essential in order to ensure that bioenergy crops have a positive and sustainable impact on climate-protection efforts. The complexity of factors relating to land-use change has led to its omission from most bioenergy life-cycle analyses but it remains an essential piece of information that governments need to consider in formulating national bioenergy policy.

In addition to the impacts of feedstock production on greenhouse gas emissions, biofuel processing and distribution can also have other environmental impacts. As in the hydrocarbon sector, the processing of biofuel feedstocks can affect local air quality with carbon monoxide, particulates, nitrogen oxide, sulphates and volatile organic compounds released by industrial processes (Dufey, 2006). However, to the extent that biofuels can replace traditional biomass such as fuelwood and charcoal, they also hold potential for dramatic improvements in human health, particularly of women and children, through reduced respiratory diseases and deaths caused by indoor air pollution.

In some cases, national regulations require importers to certify the sustainable cultivation of agricultural land, the protection of natural habitats and a minimum level of carbon dioxide savings for biofuels. Some countries and regional organizations (e.g.

the United States of America and the EU) have suggested that net greenhouse gas balances from biofuels should be in the range of 35–40 percent less than that of petrol. A careful analysis of these issues is important for all stakeholders, especially for exporters of bioenergy crops or fuels, as a basis for investment and production decisions and ensuring the marketability of their products.

Land-use change and intensification

The preceding section highlighted the influence of land-use change on the greenhouse gas balances of biofuel production. When assessing the potential emission effects of expanding biofuel production, a clear understanding is needed of the extent to which increased production will be met through improved land productivity or through expansion of cultivated area; in the latter case, the category of land is also significant. Agricultural production techniques also

---

BOX 10

Biofuels and the United Nations Framework Convention on Climate Change

Although no international agreements specifically address bioenergy, the United Nations Framework Convention on Climate Change (UNFCCC) guides Member States to "take climate-change considerations into account, to the extent feasible, in their relevant social, economic and environmental policies and actions, and employ appropriate methods ... with a view to minimizing adverse effects on the economy, on public health and on the quality of the environment of projects or measures undertaken by them to mitigate or adapt to climate change" (UNFCCC, 1992, Article 4). The Kyoto Protocol, which expires in 2012, provides a robust and modern framework for promoting clean technologies such as those for renewable energy.

The Clean Development Mechanism (CDM), as one of the flexibility mechanisms within the Kyoto Protocol, was designed to assist Parties not included in Annex 1

in achieving sustainable development and in contributing to the ultimate objective of the Convention, and to assist Parties included in Annex 1 in complying with their quantified emission limitation and emissions reduction commitments. Since the inception of the CDM in 2005, energy-industry projects have dominated all project types registered in the CDM, including those for bioenergy. Within the field of bioenergy, several methodologies are available for projects that use biomass for energy generation, although there are only a limited number of approved methodologies for biofuels. A biofuel methodology based on waste oil is already available and a methodology for biofuel production from cultivated biomass is under development.

Source: FAO, based on a contribution from the UNFCCC Secretariat.

contribute to determining greenhouse gas balances. Both factors will also determine other environmental impacts relating to soils, water and biodiversity.

Over the past five decades, most of the increase in global agricultural commodity production (around 80 percent) has resulted from yield increases, with the remainder accounted for by expansion of cropped area and increased frequency of cultivation (FAO, 2003; Hazell and Wood, 2008). The rate of growth in demand for biofuels over the past few years far exceeds historic rates of growth in demand for agricultural commodities and in crop yields. This suggests that land-use change – and the associated environmental impacts – may become a more important issue with respect to both first- and second-generation technologies. In the short term, this demand may be satisfied primarily by increasing the land area under biofuel crops while in the medium and long term the development of improved biofuel crop varieties, changes in agronomic practices and new technologies (such as cellulosic conversion) may begin to dominate. Significant yield gains and technological advances will be essential for the sustainable production of biofuel feedstocks in order to minimize rapid land-use change in areas

already under cultivation and the conversion of land not currently in crop production, such as grassland or forest land.

Area expansion

Of the world's 13.5 billion hectares of total land surface area, about 8.3 billion hectares are currently in grassland or forest and 1.6 billion hectares in cropland (Fischer, 2008). An additional 2 billion hectares are considered potentially suitable for rainfed crop production, as shown by Figure 24, although this figure should be treated with considerable caution. Much of the land in forest, wetland or other uses provides valuable environmental services, including carbon sequestration, water filtration and biodiversity preservation; thus, expansion of crop production in these areas could be detrimental to the environment.

After excluding forest land, protected areas and land needed to meet increased demand for food crops and livestock, estimates of the amount of land potentially available for expanded crop production lie between 250 and 800 million hectares, most of which is found in tropical Latin America or in Africa (Fischer, 2008).

Some of this land could be used directly for biofuel feedstock production, but

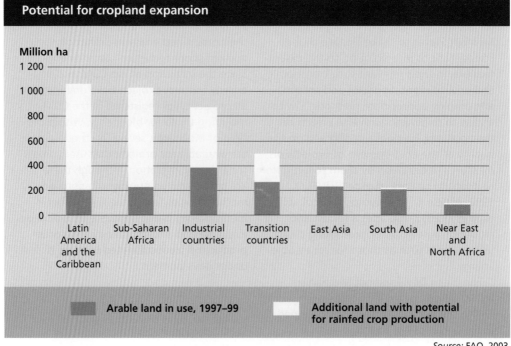

FIGURE 24
Potential for cropland expansion

Million ha

Latin America and the Caribbean — Sub-Saharan Africa — Industrial countries — Transition countries — East Asia — South Asia — Near East and North Africa

■ Arable land in use, 1997–99   □ Additional land with potential for rainfed crop production

Source: FAO, 2003.

increased biofuel production on existing cropland could also trigger expansion in the production of non-biofuel crops elsewhere. For example, increased maize production for ethanol in the central United States of America has displaced soybean on some existing cropland, which, in turn, may induce increased soybean production and conversion of grassland or forest land elsewhere. Thus, both the direct and indirect land-use changes caused by expanded biofuel production need to be considered for a full understanding of potential environmental impacts.

In 2004, an estimated 14 million hectares, worldwide, were being used to produce biofuels and their by-products, representing about 1 percent of global cropland (IEA, 2006, p. 413).[11] Sugar cane is currently cultivated on 5.6 million hectares in Brazil, and 54 percent of the crop (about 3 million hectares) is used to produce ethanol (Naylor *et al.*, 2007). United States farmers harvested 30 million hectares of maize in 2004, of which 11 percent (about 3.3 million hectares) was used for ethanol (Searchinger *et al.*, 2008). In 2007, area planted to maize in the United States of America increased by 19 percent (Naylor *et al.*, 2007; see also Westcott, 2007, p. 8). While the United States soybean area has declined by 15 percent; Brazil's soybean area is expected to increase by 6–7 percent to 43 million hectares (FAO, 2007c).

As noted in Chapter 4, land used for the production of biofuels and their by-products is projected by the IEA to expand three- to four-fold at the global level, depending on policies pursued, over the next few decades, and even more rapidly in Europe and North America. OECD–FAO (2008) projections suggest that this land will come from a global shift towards cereals over the next decade. The additional land needed will come from non-cereal croplands in Australia, Canada and the United States of America; set-aside lands in the EU or the United States Conservation Reserve Program; and new, currently uncultivated land, especially in Latin America. Some land that may not have been cultivated profitably in the past may become profitable as commodity prices rise,

and the economically feasible area would be expected to change with increased demand for biofuels and their feedstocks (Nelson and Robertson, 2008). For example, 23 million hectares were withdrawn from crop (primarily cereals) production in countries such as Kazakhstan, the Russian Federation and Ukraine following the break-up of the former Union of Soviet Socialist Republics; of these, an estimated 13 million hectares could be returned to production without major environmental cost if cereal prices and profit margins remain high and the necessary investments in handling, storage and transportation infrastructure are made (FAO, 2008e).

The sugar-cane area in Brazil is expected to almost double to 10 million hectares over the next decade; along with expansion in the Brazilian soybean area, this could displace livestock pastures and other crops, indirectly increasing pressure on uncultivated land (Naylor *et al.*, 2007). China is "committed to preventing the return to row crop production" of land enrolled in its Grain-for-Green programme, but this could increase pressure on resources in other countries, such as Cambodia and the Lao People's Democratic Republic (Naylor *et al.*, 2007).

The potential significance of indirect biofuel-induced land-use change is illustrated by a recent analysis by Searchinger *et al.* (2008). They project that maize area devoted to ethanol production in the United States of America could increase to 12.8 million hectares or more by 2016, depending on policy and market conditions. Associated reductions in the area devoted to soybean, wheat and other crops would raise prices and induce increased production in other countries. This could lead to an estimated 10.8 million hectares of additional land being brought into cultivation worldwide, including cropland expansions of 2.8 million hectares in Brazil (mostly in soybean) and 2.2 million hectares in China and India (mostly in maize and wheat). If projected cropland expansion follows the patterns observed in the 1990s, it would come primarily from forest land in Europe, Latin America, Southeast Asia and sub-Saharan Africa, and primarily from grasslands elsewhere. Critical to this scenario is the assumption that price increases will not accelerate yield growth, at least in the short term.

---

[11] Most first-generation biofuel feedstocks (e.g. maize, sugar cane, rapeseed and palm oil) cannot be distinguished by end-use at the crop production stage, so biofuel feedstock area is inferred from biofuel production data.

Other studies also highlight the possible indirect land-use changes resulting from biofuel policies (Birur, Hertel and Tyner, 2007). Meeting current biofuel mandates and targets in the EU and the United States of America would significantly increase the share of domestic feedstock production going to biofuels while reducing commodity exports and increasing demand for imports. Effects would include an expansion in land area devoted to coarse grains in Canada and the United States of America of 11–12 percent by 2010 and in the area devoted to oilseeds in Brazil, Canada and the EU of 12–21 percent. Brazilian land prices are estimated to double as a result of increased demand for grains, oilseeds and sugar cane, suggesting that EU and United States biofuel mandates could place considerable pressure on ecosystems in other parts of the world, such as the Amazon

rainforest. Banse et al. (2008) also foresee significant increases in agricultural land use, particularly in Africa and Latin America, arising from implementation of mandatory biofuel-blending policies in Canada, the EU, Japan, South Africa and the United States of America.

Intensification

While area expansion for biofuel feedstock production is likely to play a significant role in satisfying increased demand for biofuels over the next few years, the intensification of land use through improved technologies and management practices will have to complement this option, especially if production is to be sustained in the long term. Crop yield increases have historically been more significant in densely populated Asia than in sub-Saharan Africa and Latin America and more so for rice and wheat

FIGURE 25
Potential for yield increase for selected biofuel feedstock crops

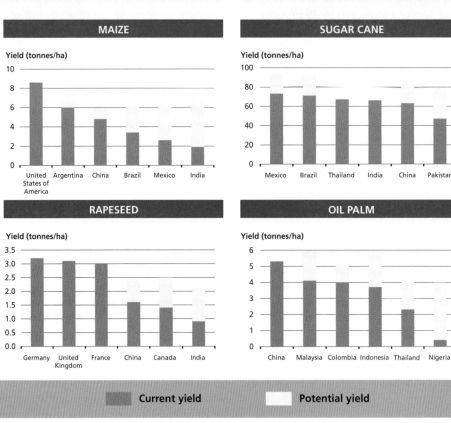

Note: In some countries, current yields exceed potential yields as a result of irrigation, multiple cropping, input use and various applied production practices.

Source: FAO.

than for maize. Large-scale public and private investment in research on improving genetic materials, input and water use and agronomic practices have played a critical role in achieving these yield gains (Hazell and Wood, 2008; Cassman *et al.*, 2005).

Despite significant gains in crop yields at the global level and in most regions, yields have lagged in sub-Saharan Africa. Actual yields are still below their potential in most regions – as shown by Figure 25 – suggesting that considerable scope remains for increased production on existing cropland. Evenson and Gollin (2003) documented a significant lag in the adoption of modern high-yielding crop varieties, particularly in Africa. Africa has also failed to keep pace with the use of other yield-enhancing technologies such as integrated nutrient and pest management, irrigation and conservation tillage.

Just as increased demand for biofuels induces direct and indirect changes in land use, it can also be expected to trigger changes in yields, both directly in the production of biofuel feedstocks and indirectly in the production of other crops – provided that appropriate investments are made to improve infrastructure, technology and access to information, knowledge and markets. A number of analytical studies are beginning to assess the changes in land use to be expected from increased biofuel demand, but little empirical evidence is yet available on which to base predictions on how yields will be affected – either directly or indirectly – or how quickly. In one example, ethanol experts in Brazil believe that, even without genetic improvements in sugar cane, yield increases in the range of 20 percent could be achieved over the next ten years simply through improved management in the production chain (Squizato, 2008).

Some of the crops currently used as feedstocks in liquid biofuel production require high-quality agricultural land and major inputs in terms of fertilizer, pesticides and water to generate economically viable yields. The degree of competition for resources between energy crops and food and fodder production will depend, among other factors, on progress in crop yields, efficiency of livestock feeds and biofuel conversion technologies. With second-generation technologies based on lignocellulosic feedstock, this competition could be reduced by the higher yields that could be realized using these newer technologies.

How will biofuel production affect water, soils and biodiversity?

The intensification of agricultural production systems for biofuel feedstocks and the conversion of existing and new croplands will have environmental effects beyond their impacts on greenhouse gas emissions. The nature and extent of these impacts are dependent on factors such as scale of production, type of feedstock, cultivation and land-management practices, location and downstream processing routes. Evidence remains limited on the impacts specifically associated with intensified biofuel production, although most of the problems are similar to those already associated with agricultural production – water depletion and pollution, soil degradation, nutrient depletion and the loss of wild and agricultural biodiversity.

Impacts on water resources

Water, rather than land, scarcity may prove to be the key limiting factor for biofuel feedstock production in many contexts. About 70 percent of freshwater withdrawn worldwide is used for agricultural purposes (Comprehensive Assessment of Water Management in Agriculture, 2007). Water resources for agriculture are becoming increasingly scarce in many countries as a result of increased competition with domestic or industrial uses. Moreover, the expected impacts of climate change in terms of reduced rainfall and runoff in some key producer regions (including the Near East, North Africa and South Asia) will place further pressure on already scarce resources.

Biofuels currently account for about 100 km^3 (or 1 percent) of all water transpired by crops worldwide, and about 44 km^3 (or 2 percent) of all irrigation water withdrawals (de Fraiture, Giordano and Yongsong, 2007). Many of the crops currently used for biofuel production – such as sugar cane, oil palm and maize – have relatively high water requirements at commercial yield levels (see

Table 10) and are therefore best suited to high-rainfall tropical areas, unless they can be irrigated. (Rainfed production of biofuel feedstocks is significant in Brazil, where 76 percent of sugar-cane production is under rainfed conditions, and in the United States of America, where 70 percent of maize production is rainfed.) Even perennial plants such as jatropha and pongamia that can be grown in semi-arid areas on marginal or degraded lands may require some irrigation during hot and dry summers. Further, the processing of feedstocks into biofuels can use large quantities of water, mainly for washing plants and seeds and for evaporative cooling. However, it is irrigated production of these key biofuel feedstocks that will have the greatest impact on local water resource balances. Many irrigated sugar-producing regions in southern and eastern Africa and northeastern Brazil are already operating near the hydrological limits of their associated river basins. The Awash, Limpopo, Maputo, Nile and São Francisco river basins are cases in point.

While the potential for expansion of irrigated areas may appear high in some areas on the basis of water resources and land, the actual scope for increased biofuel production under irrigated conditions on existing or new irrigated lands is limited by infrastructural requirements to guarantee water deliveries and by land-tenure systems that may not conform with commercialized production systems. Equally, expansion may be constrained by higher marginal costs of water storage (the most economic sites have already been taken) and land acquisition. Figure 26 shows that the potential for growth for the Near East and North Africa region is reaching its limit. While there remains an abundance

of water resources in South Asia and East and Southeast Asia, there is very little land available for extra irrigated agriculture. Most potential for expansion is limited to Latin America and sub-Saharan Africa. However, in the latter region it is expected that the current low levels of irrigation water withdrawals will increase only slowly.

Producing more biofuel crops will affect water quality as well as quantity. Converting pastures or woodlands into maize fields, for example, may exacerbate problems such as soil erosion, sedimentation and excess nutrient (nitrogen and phosphorous) runoff into surface waters, and infiltration into groundwater from increased fertilizer application. Excess nitrogen in the Mississippi river system is a major cause of the oxygen-starved "dead zone" in the Gulf of Mexico, where many forms of marine life cannot survive. Runge and Senauer (2007) argue that as maize–soybean rotations are displaced by maize cropped continuously for ethanol production in the United States of America, major increases in nitrogen fertilizer application and runoff will aggravate these problems.

Biodiesel and ethanol production results in organically contaminated wastewater that, if released untreated, could increase eutrophication of surface waterbodies. However, existing wastewater treatment technologies can deal effectively with organic pollutants and wastes. Fermentation systems can reduce the biological oxygen demand of wastewater by more than 90 percent, so that water can be reused for processing, and methane can be captured in the treatment system and used for power generation. As regards the distribution and storage phases of the cycle, because

TABLE 10

Water requirements for biofuel crops

CROP	Annual obtainable fuel yield	Energy yield	Evapotranspiration equivalent	Potential crop evapotranspiration	Rainfed crop evapotranspiration	Irrigated crop water requirement	
	(Litres/ha)	(GJ/ha)	(Litres/litre fuel)	(mm/ha)	(mm/ha)	(mm/ha)[1]	(Litres/litre fuel)
Sugar cane	6 000	120	2 000	1 400	1 000	800	1 333
Maize	3 500	70	1 357	550	400	300	857
Oil palm	5 500	193	2 364	1 500	1 300	0	0
Rapeseed	1 200	42	3 333	500	400	0	0

[1] On the assumption of 50 percent irrigation efficiency.

Source: FAO.

ethanol and biodiesel are biodegradable, the potential for negative impacts on soil and water from leakage and spills is reduced compared with that of fossil fuels.

In Brazil, where sugar cane for ethanol is grown primarily under rainfed conditions, water availability is not a constraint, but water pollution associated with the application of fertilizers and agrochemicals, soil erosion, sugar-cane washing and other steps in the ethanol production process are major concerns (Moreira, 2007). Most milling wastewater (vinasse) is used for irrigation and fertilization of the sugar-cane plantations, thus reducing both water demands and eutrophication risks.

Pesticides and other chemicals can wash into waterbodies, negatively affecting water quality. Maize, soybeans and other biofuel feedstocks differ markedly in their fertilizer and pesticide requirements. Of the principal feedstocks, maize is subject to the highest application rates of both fertilizer and pesticides per hectare. Per unit of energy gained, biofuels from soybean and other low-input, high-diversity prairie biomass are estimated to require only a fraction of the nitrogen, phosphorus and pesticides required by maize, with correspondingly lower impacts

on water quality (Hill et al., 2006; Tilman, Hill and Lehman, 2006).

Impacts on soil resources

Both land-use change and intensification of agricultural production on existing croplands can have significant adverse impacts on soils, but these impacts – just as for any crop – depend critically on farming techniques. Inappropriate cultivation practices can reduce soil organic matter and increase soil erosion by removing permanent soil cover. The removal of plant residues can reduce soil nutrient contents and increase greenhouse gas emissions through losses of soil carbon.

On the other hand, conservation tillage, crop rotations and other improved management practices can, under the right conditions, reduce adverse impacts or even improve environmental quality in conjunction with increased biofuel feedstock production. Growing perennials such as palm, short-rotation coppice, sugar cane or switchgrass instead of annual crops can improve soil quality by increasing soil cover and organic carbon levels. In combination with no-tillage and reduced fertilizer and pesticide inputs, positive impacts on biodiversity can be obtained.

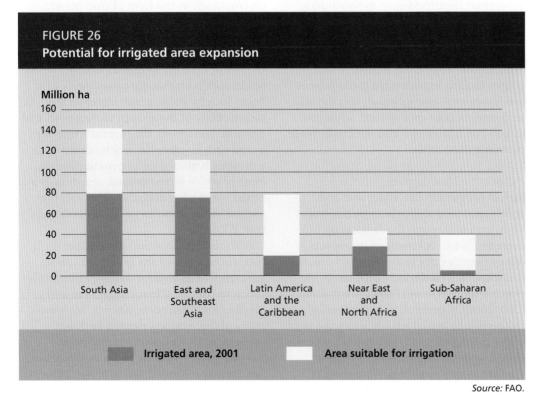

FIGURE 26
Potential for irrigated area expansion

Million ha

Source: FAO.

Different feedstocks vary in terms of their soil impacts, nutrient demand and the extent of land preparation they require. The IEA (2006, p. 393) notes that the impact of sugar cane on soils is generally less than that of rapeseed, maize and other cereals. Soil quality is maintained by recycling nutrients from sugar-mill and distillery wastes, but using more bagasse as an energy input to ethanol production would reduce recycling. Extensive production systems require re-use of residues to recycle nutrients and maintain soil fertility; typically only 25–33 percent of available crop residues from grasses or maize can be harvested sustainably (Doornbosch and Steenblik, 2007, p. 15, citing Wilhelm *et al.*, 2007). By creating a market for agricultural residues, increased demand for energy could, if not properly managed, divert residues to the production of biofuels, with potentially detrimental effects on soil quality, especially on soil organic matter (Fresco, 2007).

Hill *et al.* (2006) found that the production of soybean for biodiesel in the United States of America requires much less fertilizer and pesticide per unit of energy produced than does maize. But they argue that both feedstocks require higher input levels and better-quality land than would second-generation feedstocks such as switchgrass, woody plants or diverse mixtures of prairie grasses and forbs (see also Tilman, Hill and Lehman, 2006). Perennial lignocellulosic crops such as eucalyptus, poplar, willow or grasses require less-intensive management and fewer fossil-energy inputs and can also be grown on poor-quality land, while soil carbon and quality will also tend to increase over time (IEA, 2006).

Impacts on biodiversity

Biofuel production can affect wild and agricultural biodiversity in some positive ways, such as through the restoration of degraded lands, but many of its impacts will be negative, for example when natural landscapes are converted into energy-crop plantations or peat lands are drained (CBD, 2008). In general, wild biodiversity is threatened by loss of habitat when the area under crop production is expanded, whereas agricultural biodiversity is vulnerable in the case of large-scale monocropping, which is based on a narrow pool of genetic

material and can also lead to reduced use of traditional varieties.

The first pathway for biodiversity loss is habitat loss following land conversion for crop production, for example from forest or grassland. As the CBD (2008) notes, many current biofuel crops are well suited for tropical areas. This increases the economic incentives in countries with biofuel production potential to convert natural ecosystems into feedstock plantations (e.g. oil palm), causing a loss of wild biodiversity in these areas. While oil palm plantations do not need much fertilizer or pesticide, even on poor soils, their expansion can lead to loss of rainforests. Although loss of natural habitats through land conversion for biofuel feedstock production has been reported in some countries (Curran *et al.*, 2004; Soyka, Palmer and Engel, 2007), the data and analysis needed to assess its extent and consequences are still lacking. Nelson and Robertson (2008) examined how rising commodity prices caused by increased biofuel demand could induce land-use change and intensification in Brazil, and found that agricultural expansion driven by higher prices could endanger areas rich in bird species diversity.

The second major pathway is loss of agrobiodiversity, induced by intensification on croplands, in the form of crop genetic uniformity. Most biofuel feedstock plantations are based on a single species. There are also concerns about low levels of genetic diversity in grasses used as feedstocks, such as sugar cane (The Royal Society, 2008), which increases the susceptibility of these crops to new pests and diseases. Conversely, the reverse is true for a crop such as jatropha, which possesses an extremely high degree of genetic diversity, most of which is unimproved, resulting in a broad range of genetic characteristics that undermine its commercial value (IFAD/FAO/UNF, 2008).

With respect to second-generation feedstocks, some of the promoted species are classified as invasive species, raising new concerns over how to manage them and avoid unintended consequences. Moreover, many of the enzymes needed for their conversion are genetically modified to increase their efficiency and would need to be carefully managed within closed industrial production processes (CFC, 2007).

Positive effects on biodiversity have been noted in degraded or marginal areas where new perennial mixed species have been introduced to restore ecosystem functioning and increase biodiversity (CBD, 2008). Experimental data from test plots on degraded and abandoned soils (Tilman, Hill and Lehman, 2006) show that low-input high-diversity mixtures of native grassland perennials – which offer a range of ecosystem services, including wildlife habitat, water filtration and carbon sequestration – also produce higher net energy gains (measured as energy released on combustion), greater greenhouse gas emission reductions and less agrichemical pollution than do maize-ethanol or soybean-biodiesel and that performance increases with the number of species. The authors of this study also found that switchgrass can be highly productive on fertile soils, especially when fertilizer and pesticides are applied, but that its performance on poor soils does not match that of diverse native perennials.

Can biofuels be produced on marginal lands?

Marginal or degraded lands are often characterized by lack of water, which constrains both plant growth and nutrient availability, and by low soil fertility and high temperatures. Common problems in these areas include vegetation degradation, water and wind erosion, salinization, soil compaction and crusting, and soil-nutrient depletion. Pollution, acidification, alkalization and waterlogging may also occur in some locations.

Biofuel crops that can tolerate environmental conditions where food crops might fail may offer the opportunity to put to productive use land that presently yields few economic benefits. Crops such as cassava, castor, sweet sorghum, jatropha and pongamia are potential candidates, as are tree crops that tolerate dry conditions, such as eucalyptus. It is important to note, however, that marginal lands often provide subsistence services to the rural poor, including many agricultural activities performed by women. Whether the poor stand to benefit or suffer from

the introduction of biofuel production on marginal lands depends critically on the nature and security of their rights to land.

It is not unusual to hear claims that significant tracts of marginal land exist that could be dedicated to biofuel production, thus reducing the conflict with food crops and offering a new source of income to poor farmers. Although such lands would be less productive and subject to higher risks, using them for bioenergy plantations could have secondary benefits, such as restoration of degraded vegetation, carbon sequestration and local environmental services. In most countries, however, the suitability of this land for sustainable biofuel production is poorly documented.

Growing any crop on marginal land with low levels of water and nutrient inputs will result in lower yields. Drought-tolerant jatropha and sweet sorghum are no exception. To produce commercially acceptable yield levels, plant and tree species cannot be stressed beyond certain limits; in fact, they will benefit from modest levels of additional inputs. Thus, while improved crops may offer potential over the longer term, adequate nutrients, water and management are still needed to ensure economically meaningful yields – implying that even hardy crops grown on marginal lands will still compete to some extent with food crops for resources such as nutrients and water.

Numerous studies confirm that the value of the higher economic yields from good agricultural land usually outweighs any additional costs. Thus, there is a strong likelihood that sustained demand for biofuels would intensify the pressure on the good lands where higher returns could be realized (Azar and Larson, 2000).

Ensuring environmentally sustainable biofuel production

Good practices
Good practices aim to apply available knowledge to address the sustainability dimensions of on-farm biofuel feedstock production, harvesting and processing. This aim applies to natural-resource management issues such as land, soil, water and biodiversity as well as to the life-cycle analysis used to estimate greenhouse gas

BOX 11
Jatropha – a "miracle" crop?

As an energy crop, *Jatropha curcas* (L.) (jatropha) is making a lot of headlines. The plant is drought-tolerant, grows well on marginal land, needs only moderate rainfall of between 300 and 1 000 mm per year, is easy to establish, can help reclaim eroded land and grows quickly. These characteristics appeal to many developing countries that are concerned about diminishing tree cover and soil fertility and are looking for an energy crop that minimizes competition with food crops. At the same time, this small tree produces seeds after two to five years containing 30 percent oil by kernel weight – oil that is already being used to make soap, candles and cosmetics and has similar medicinal properties to castor oil, but is also useful for cooking and electricity generation.

A native of northern Latin/Central America, there are three varieties of jatropha: Nicaraguan, Mexican (distinguished by its less- or non-toxic seed) and Cape Verde. The third of these varieties became established in Cape Verde and from there spread to parts of Africa and Asia. On Cape Verde it was grown on a large scale for export to Portugal for oil extraction and soap-making. At its peak, in 1910, jatropha exports reached over 5 600 tonnes (Heller, 1996).

The many positive attributes claimed for jatropha have translated into numerous projects for large-scale oil and/or biodiesel production as well as small-scale rural development. International and national investors are rushing to establish large areas for jatropha cultivation in Belize, Brazil, China, Egypt, Ethiopia, the Gambia, Honduras, India, Indonesia, Mozambique, Myanmar, the Philippines, Senegal and the United Republic of Tanzania. The largest-scale venture is the Indian Government's "National Mission" to cultivate jatropha on 400 000 hectares within the period 2003–07 (Gonsalves, 2006). By 2011–12, the goal is to replace 20 percent of diesel consumption with biodiesel produced from jatropha, cultivated on around 10 million hectares of wasteland and generating year-round employment for 5 million people (Gonsalves, 2006; Francis, Edinger and Becker, 2005). The original target may well be ambitious, as Euler and Gorriz (2004) report that probably only a fraction of the initial 400 000 hectares allocated to jatropha by the Indian Government is actually under cultivation.

The plant also grows widely in Africa, often as hedges separating properties in towns and villages. In Mali, thousands of kilometres of jatropha hedges can be found; they protect gardens from livestock and can also help reduce damage and erosion from wind and water. The seed is already used for soap-making and medicinal purposes, and jatropha oil is now also being promoted by a non-

emissions and determine whether a specific biofuel is more climate-change friendly than a fossil fuel. In practical terms, soil, water and crop protection; energy and water management; nutrient and agrochemical management; biodiversity and landscape conservation; harvesting, processing and distribution all count among the areas where good practices are needed to address sustainable bioenergy development.

Conservation agriculture is one practice that sets out to achieve sustainable and profitable agriculture for farmers and rural people by employing minimum soil disturbance, permanent organic soil cover and diversified crop rotations. In the context of the current focus on carbon storage and on technologies that reduce energy intensity it seems especially appropriate. The approach also proves responsive to situations where labour is scarce and there is a need to conserve soil moisture and fertility. Interventions such as mechanical soil tillage are reduced to a minimum, and inputs such as agrochemicals and nutrients of mineral or organic origin are applied at an optimum level and in amounts that do not disrupt biological processes. Conservation agriculture has been shown to be effective across a variety of agro-ecological zones and farming systems.

governmental organization to power multifunctional platforms, a slow-speed diesel engine containing an oil expeller, a generator, a small battery charger and a grinding mill (UNDP, 2004). Pilot projects promoting jatropha oil as an energy source for small-scale rural electrification projects are under way in the United Republic of Tanzania and other African countries.

Despite considerable investment and projects being undertaken in many countries, reliable scientific data on the agronomy of jatropha are not available. Information on the relationship between yields and variables such as soil, climate, crop management and crop genetic material on which to base investment decisions is poorly documented. What evidence there is shows a wide range of yields that cannot be linked to relevant parameters such as soil fertility and water availability (Jongschaap *et al.*, 2007). Experience with jatropha plantations in the 1990s, such as the "Proyecto Tempate" in Nicaragua, which ran from 1991 to 1999, ended in failure (Euler and Gorriz, 2004).

Indeed, it appears that the many positive claims for the plant are not based on mature project experiences. Jongschaap *et al.* (2007) argue that, on a modest scale, jatropha cultivation can help with soil-water conservation,

soil reclamation and erosion control, and be used for living fences, firewood, green manure, lighting fuel, local soap production, insecticides and medicinal applications. However, they conclude that claims of high oil yields in combination with low nutrient requirements (soil fertility), lower water use, low labour inputs, the non-existence of competition with food production and tolerance to pests and diseases are unsupported by scientific evidence. The most critical gaps are the lack of improved varieties and available seed. Jatropha has not yet been domesticated as a crop with reliable performance.

The fear that the rush into jatropha on the basis of unrealistic expectations will not only lead to financial losses but also undermine confidence among local communities – a recurrent theme in many African countries – appears to be well founded. Sustainable jatropha plantations will mean taking the uncertainty out of production and marketing. Further research is needed on suitable germplasm and on yields under different conditions, and markets need to be established to promote sustainable development of the crop.

Good farming practices coupled with good forestry practices could greatly reduce the environmental costs associated with the possible promotion of sustainable intensification at forest margins. Approaches based on agro-silvo-pasture-livestock integration could be considered also when bioenergy crops form part of the mix.

Standards, sustainability criteria and compliance

Although the multiple and diverse environmental impacts of bioenergy development do not differ substantively from those of other forms of agriculture,

the question remains of how they can best be assessed and reflected in field activities. Existing environmental impact-assessment techniques and strategic environmental assessments offer a good starting point for analysing the biophysical factors. There also exists a wealth of technical knowledge drawn from agricultural development during the past 60 years. New contributions from the bioenergy context include analytical frameworks for bioenergy and food security and for bioenergy impact analysis (FAO, forthcoming (a) and (b)); work on the aggregate environmental impacts, including soil acidification, excessive fertilizer use, biodiversity loss, air pollution and pesticide toxicity (Zah *et al.*, 2007); and work on social and environmental sustainability criteria, including limits on deforestation, competition with food production, adverse impacts on biodiversity, soil erosion and nutrient leaching (Faaij, 2007).

The biofuel sector is characterized by a wide range of stakeholders with diverse interests. This, combined with the rapid evolution of the sector, has led to a proliferation of initiatives to ensure sustainable bioenergy development. Principles, criteria and requirements are under consideration among many private and public groups, along with compliance mechanisms to assess performance and guide development of the sector. The Global Bioenergy Partnership's task forces on greenhouse gas methodologies and on sustainability, and the round table on sustainable biofuels, count among these, together with many other public, private and non-profit efforts. Such diversity suggests that a process for harmonizing the various approaches may be needed, especially in the light of policy mandates and targets that serve to stimulate further biofuel production.

Most of the criteria are currently being developed in industrialized countries and are aimed at ensuring that biofuels are produced, distributed and used in an environmentally sustainable manner before they are traded in international markets. The European Commission, for example, has already proposed criteria that it considers to be compatible with WTO rules (personal communication, E. Deurwaarder, European Commission, 2008). However, to date none have yet been tested, especially in conjunction with government support schemes such as subsidies or when designated for preferential treatment under international trade agreements (Doornbosch and Steenblik, 2007; UNCTAD, 2008).

The term "standards" implies rigorous systems for measuring parameters against defined criteria, in which failure to comply would prevent a country from exporting its product. Such internationally agreed systems already exist for a range of food safety, chemical and human health topics. Is the biofuel sector sufficiently developed for the establishment of such a system and are the risks sufficiently great that its absence would pose significant, irreversible threats to human health or the environment? Should biofuels be treated more stringently than other agricultural commodities?

On the one hand, given that most environmental impacts of biofuels are indistinguishable from those of increased agricultural production in general, it could be argued that equal standards should be applied across the board. Furthermore, restricting land-use change could foreclose opportunities for developing countries to benefit from increased demand for agricultural commodities. On the other hand, there are also strong arguments that agricultural producers and policy-makers should learn from earlier mistakes and avoid the negative environmental impacts that have accompanied agricultural land conversion and intensification in the past.

Solutions to this dilemma will require careful dialogue and negotiation among countries if the combined goals of agricultural productivity growth and environmental sustainability are to be achieved. A starting point might be found by establishing best practices for sustainable production of biofuels, which can then also help transform farming practices for non-biofuel crops. In time, and accompanied by capacity-building efforts for the countries that need it, more stringent standards and certification systems could be established.

One option to explore could be payments for environmental services in combination with biofuel production. Payments for environmental services were discussed in detail in the 2007 edition of *The State of Food and Agriculture*. This mechanism would compensate farmers for providing specific environmental services using production methods that are environmentally more sustainable. Payments could be linked to compliance with standards and certification schemes agreed at the international level. Payment schemes for environmental services, although challenging and complicated to implement, could constitute a further tool to ensure that biofuels are produced in a sustainable manner.

Key messages of the chapter

- Biofuels are only one component of a range of alternatives for mitigating greenhouse gas emissions. Depending on the policy objectives, other options may prove more cost-effective, including different forms of renewable energy, increased energy efficiency and conservation, and reduced emissions from deforestation and land degradation.
- Notwithstanding that the impacts of increased biofuel production on greenhouse gas emissions, land, water and biodiversity vary widely across countries, biofuels, feedstocks and production practices, there is a strong and immediate need for harmonized approaches to life-cycle analysis, greenhouse gas balances and sustainability criteria.
- Greenhouse gas balances are not positive for all feedstocks. For climate-change purposes, investment should be directed towards crops that have the highest positive greenhouse gas balances with the lowest environmental and social costs.
- Environmental impacts can be generated at all stages of biofuel feedstock production and processing, but processes related to land-use change and intensification tend to dominate. Over the next decade, rapid policy-driven growth in demand for biofuels is likely to accelerate the conversion of non-agricultural lands to crop production. This will occur directly for biofuel feedstock production and indirectly for other crops displaced from existing cropland.
- Yield increases and careful use of inputs will be essential components in alleviating land-use pressure from both food and energy crops. Dedicated research, investment in technology and strengthened institutions and infrastructure will be required.
- Environmental impacts vary widely across feedstocks, production practices and locations, and depend critically on how land-use change is managed. Replacing annual crops with perennial feedstocks (such as oil palm, jatropha or perennial grasses) can improve soil carbon balances, but converting tropical forests for crop production of any kind can release quantities of greenhouse gases that far exceed potential annual savings from biofuels.
- Availability of water resources, limited by technical and institutional factors, will constrain the amount of biofuel feedstock production in countries that would otherwise have a comparative advantage in their production.
- Regulatory approaches to standards and certification may not be the first or best option for ensuring broad-based and equitable participation in biofuel production. Systems that incorporate best practices and capacity building may yield better short-term results and provide the flexibility needed to adapt to changing circumstances. Payments for environmental services may also represent an instrument for encouraging compliance with sustainable production methods.
- Biofuel feedstocks and other food and agricultural crops should be treated similarly. The environmental concerns over biofuel feedstock production are the same as for the impacts of increased agricultural production in general; therefore measures to ensure sustainability should be applied consistently to all crops.
- Good agricultural practices, such as conservation agriculture, can reduce the carbon footprint and the adverse environmental impacts of biofuel production – just as they can for extensive agricultural production in general. Perennial feedstock crops, such as grasses or trees, can diversify production systems and help improve marginal or degraded land.
- Domestic government policy must become better informed of the international consequences of biofuel development. International dialogue, often through existing mechanisms, can help formulate realistic and achievable biofuel mandates and targets.

6. Impacts on poverty and food security

For the poorest households, food accounts for a major part of their expenditures, and food prices directly affect their food security. As a commonly accepted definition, food insecurity exists when people lack secure access to sufficient amounts of safe and nutritious food for normal growth and development and an active, healthy life. Already, the recent increase in staple food prices has triggered demonstrations and riots in a number of countries. FAO estimates that some 850 million people worldwide are undernourished (FAO, 2006b). Given the potential scale of the biofuel market, the uncertainty relating to long-term price developments and the large number of poor households, the question of what impact expanding biofuel production will have on the food security of the poor should be high on the political agenda.

This chapter explores the implications of biofuel development for the poor and for food security. Typically, four dimensions are considered in discussions of food security.

- **Availability of food** is determined by domestic production, import capacity, existence of food stocks and food aid.
- **Access to food** depends on levels of poverty, purchasing power of households, prices and the existence of transport and market infrastructure and food distribution systems.
- **Stability** of supply and access may be affected by weather, price fluctuations, human-induced disasters and a variety of political and economic factors.
- Safe and healthy **food utilization** depends on care and feeding, food safety and quality, access to clean water, health and sanitation.

Although expanding demand for biofuels is only one of many factors underlying the recent price increases (see Chapter 4, page 41) the rapid growth in biofuel production will affect food security at the national and household levels mainly through its impact on food prices and incomes. In terms of the four dimensions, the discussion focuses on the impacts of higher food prices on availability and access at the national level, as well as the household level. At both levels, the initial focus is on short-term impacts, before moving on to address the longer-term impacts. In the medium-to-longer term, higher agricultural prices offer the potential for a supply response and for strengthening and revitalizing the role of agriculture as an engine of growth in developing countries.[12]

Food-security impacts at the national level

Chapter 3 discussed the strengthened linkages between energy and agricultural commodity prices resulting from the growth in demand for biofuels and Chapter 4 considered the implications for agricultural commodity prices. How individual countries will be affected by higher prices will depend on whether they are net agricultural commodity importers or net exporters. Some countries will benefit from higher prices, but the least-developed countries,[13] which have been experiencing a widening agricultural trade deficit over the last two decades (Figure 27), are expected to be considerably worse off.

Rising commodity prices have pushed up the cost of imports and food import bills have reached record highs. Based on FAO's latest analysis, global expenditures on

---

[12] The dynamics of the rapid rise in commodity prices are covered in greater detail in *The State of Agricultural Commodity Markets 2008* (FAO, forthcoming, 2008c), while the impacts of soaring food prices on the poor are the subject of *The State of Food Insecurity in the World* (FAO, forthcoming, 2008d).

[13] Least-developed countries are classified as such on the basis of: (a) a low-income criterion (a three-year average estimate of per capita gross national income of below US$750); (b) a human-resource weakness criterion; and (c) an economic vulnerability criterion. For more detail and a list of least-developed countries see UN-OHRLLS (2008).

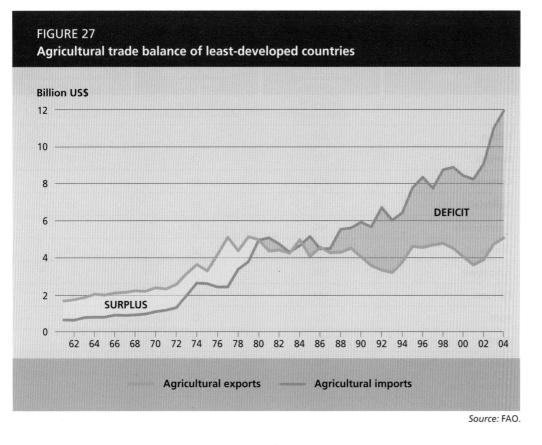

FIGURE 27
Agricultural trade balance of least-developed countries

Billion US$

SURPLUS

DEFICIT

Agricultural exports   Agricultural imports

Source: FAO.

imported foodstuffs in 2007 rose by about 29 percent above the record of the previous year (FAO, 2008a) (Table 11). The bulk of the increase was accounted for by rising prices of imported cereals and vegetable oils – commodity groups that feature heavily in biofuel production. More expensive feed ingredients lead to higher prices for meat and dairy products, raising the expenditures on imports of those commodities. The rise of international freight rates to new highs also affected the import value of all

TABLE 11
Import bills of total food and major food commodities for 2007 and their percentage increase over 2006

COMMODITY	WORLD		DEVELOPING COUNTRIES		LDCs[1]		LIFDCs[2]	
	2007	Increase over 2006	2007	Increase over 2006	2007	Increase over 2006	2007	Increase over 2006
	(US$ million)	(Percentage)	(US$ million)	(Percentage)	(US$ million)	(Percentage)	(US$ million)	(Percentage)
Cereals	268 300	44	100 441	35	8 031	32	41 709	33
Vegetable oils	114 077	61	55 658	60	3 188	64	38 330	67
Meat	89 712	14	20 119	18	1 079	24	8 241	31
Dairy	86 393	90	25 691	89	1 516	84	9 586	89
Sugar	22 993	–30	11 904	–14	1 320	–25	4 782	–37
Total food	812 743	29	253 626	33	17 699	28	119 207	35

[1] Least-developed countries (see footnote 13).
[2] Low-income food-deficit countries. FAO classifies countries as low-income food-deficit on the basis of three criteria: their per-capita income; their net food trade position; and a "persistence of position", which postpones the "exit" of an LIFDC from the list, despite the country not meeting the LIFDC income criterion or the food-deficit criterion, until the change in its status is verified for three consecutive years.
For a detailed description of the criteria and a list of LIFDC countries, see: http://www.fao.org/countryprofiles/lifdc.asp.
Source: FAO, 2008a.

TABLE 12
Net importers of petroleum products and major cereals, ranked by prevalence of undernourishment

COUNTRY	PETROLEUM IMPORTED	MAJOR CEREALS IMPORTED	PREVALENCE OF UNDERNOURISHMENT
	(Percentage of consumption)	(Percentage of domestic production)	(Percentage of population)
Eritrea	100	88	75
Burundi	100	12	66
Comoros	100	80	60
Tajikistan	99	43	56
Sierra Leone	100	53	51
Liberia	100	62	50
Zimbabwe	100	2	47
Ethiopia	100	22	46
Haiti	100	72	46
Zambia	100	4	46
Central African Republic	100	25	44
Mozambique	100	20	44
United Republic of Tanzania	100	14	44
Guinea-Bissau	100	55	39
Madagascar	100	14	38
Malawi	100	7	35
Cambodia	100	5	33
Democratic People's Republic of Korea	98	45	33
Rwanda	100	29	33
Botswana	100	76	32
Niger	100	82	32
Kenya	100	20	31

Source: FAO, 2008a.

commodities, placing additional pressure on the ability of countries to cover their food import bills. Although growing demand for biofuels accounts for only part of the recent sharp price increases, the table nevertheless illustrates the significant impact higher agricultural commodity prices can have, especially on the low-income food-deficit countries (LIFDCs).

High food prices have been accompanied by rising fuel prices, which further threaten macroeconomic stability and overall growth, especially of low-income

net energy-importing countries. Table 12 lists 22 countries considered especially vulnerable owing to a combination of high levels of chronic hunger (above 30 percent undernourishment), high dependency on imports of petroleum products (100 percent in most countries) and, in many cases, high dependency on imports of major cereals (rice, wheat and maize) for domestic consumption. Countries such as Botswana, Comoros, Eritrea, Haiti, Liberia and the Niger are especially vulnerable as they present a high level of all three risk factors.

Food-security impacts at the household level – short-run effects[14]

Access to food

At the household level, a critical factor for food security is access to food. Access to food refers to the ability of households to produce or purchase sufficient food for their needs. Two key indicators can help assess the impact of biofuel developments on food security: food prices and household incomes. The more income a household or individual has, the more food (and of better quality) can be purchased. The precise effects of food prices on household food security are more complex. Higher food prices are expected to make net food-buying households in both urban and rural areas worse off, while better-endowed rural households, who are net sellers of food, stand to gain from the increased incomes resulting from the higher prices.

Higher world food prices do not necessarily affect household food security: the impact will depend on the extent to which international prices pass through to domestic markets. The depreciation of the United States dollar against many currencies (for example the euro and the CFA [Communauté financière africaine] franc) and government policies designed to avoid large domestic price shocks tend to reduce the transmission of world market prices to domestic markets.[15] Sharma (2002), in a study of eight Asian countries in the 1990s, found that price transmission was strongest for maize, followed by wheat, and least for rice, which is the staple food for most of Asia's poor. The degree of transmission is always stronger over the longer term.

In many Asian countries rice is designated as a special, or sensitive, commodity for food security, and FAO (2008f) found that transmission varies significantly from country to country, depending on the instruments, if any, that are used to insulate

the domestic economy from price increases on international markets. For example, India and the Philippines make use of government storage, procurement and distribution as well as restrictions on international trade. Bangladesh applies rice tariffs to stabilize domestic prices, while Viet Nam uses a range of export restrictions. On the other hand, countries such as China and Thailand have allowed most of the changes in world prices to pass through to domestic markets. Maize is a feedgrain in Asia and subject to much less price intervention. FAO (2004b) found that price transmission is generally weaker in Africa than in Asian countries. Domestic price policies can help stabilize prices but they do require fiscal resources. In the longer run they may also impede or slow down an effective supply response to higher prices.

Impacts on net food buyers and net food sellers
While almost all urban dwellers are net food consumers, not all rural dwellers are net food producers. Many smallholders and agricultural labourers are net purchasers of food, as they do not own sufficient land to produce enough food for their families. Empirical evidence from a number of sub-Saharan African countries, compiled in Barrett (forthcoming) in no case finds a majority of farmers or rural households (depending on the survey definition) to be net food sellers.

Empirical evidence prepared by FAO (2008a) confirms this pattern, as illustrated in Table 13, which shows the share of net staple food-selling households among urban and rural households, respectively, for a series of countries. Only in two instances does the share of net selling households exceed 50 percent.

Even in rural areas, where agriculture and staple food production is an important occupation for the majority of the poor, a vast share of the poor are net food buyers (Figure 28) and thus stand to lose, or at least not gain, from an increase in the price of tradable staple foods. The proportion of poor smallholders that are also net sellers never exceeds 37 percent and for four of the seven countries is 13 percent or less. The proportion of poor that are net buyers ranges from 45.7 percent in Cambodia to over 87 percent in Bolivia, and for

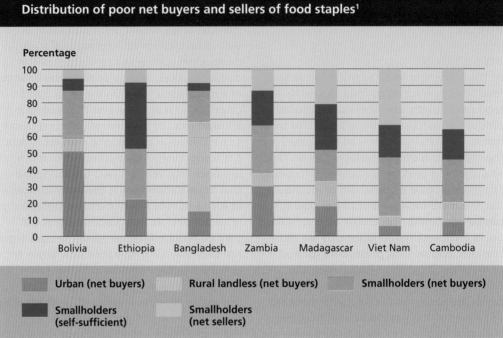

FIGURE 28
Distribution of poor net buyers and sellers of food staples[1]

Percentage

Countries (x-axis): Bolivia, Ethiopia, Bangladesh, Zambia, Madagascar, Viet Nam, Cambodia

Legend:
- Urban (net buyers)
- Rural landless (net buyers)
- Smallholders (net buyers)
- Smallholders (self-sufficient)
- Smallholders (net sellers)

[1] Percentage of poor population buying or selling internationally traded staples (rice, wheat, maize, beans).

Source: World Bank, 2007.

five of the seven countries the proportion is over 50 percent.

Poverty impacts of higher food prices
For the poorest households, food typically accounts for half, and often more, of their total expenditure. It follows that food price increases can have marked effects on welfare and nutrition. As an example, Block *et al.* (2004) found that when rice prices increased in Indonesia in the late 1990s, mothers in poor families responded by reducing their caloric intake in order to feed their children better, leading to an increase in maternal wasting. Furthermore, purchases of more nutritious foods were reduced in order to afford the more expensive rice. This led to a measurable decline in blood haemoglobin levels in young children (and in their mothers), increasing the probability of developmental damage.

Farmers who are net food sellers and will benefit from higher prices will typically be those with more land, who will also tend to be better off than farmers with only little land. Moreover, farmers with more surplus production to sell will benefit from high prices more than farmers with only a small surplus to sell. In any case, poorer farmers are

unlikely to receive the bulk of the benefits from higher food prices and are the most likely to be negatively affected.

Estimates of the short-term welfare impact on rural and urban households of a 10 percent increase in price of the main staple food are shown in Figure 29 for seven of the countries listed in Table 13. These estimates do not allow for household responses in production and consumption decisions and thus they represent an upper bound of the likely impact. However, in the very short run, the potential for adjustments in crop production is limited, and on the consumption side the very poor are likely to have only minimal substitution possibilities.

What Figure 29 highlights is that the poorest expenditure quintiles are worst affected in both urban and rural areas – they experience either the largest decline or the smallest increase in welfare. Even in some of the countries where rural households gain on average, for example Pakistan and Viet Nam, the poorest quintiles in the rural areas still face a negative change in welfare as a result of the staple price increase. Unsurprisingly, all urban households are expected to lose in all countries, but to varying degrees, with the poorest experiencing the largest decline.

TABLE 13
Share of net staple food-seller households among urban, rural and total households

COUNTRY/YEAR	SHARE OF HOUSEHOLDS		
	Urban	Rural	All
	(Percentage)	(Percentage)	(Percentage)
Bangladesh, 2000	3.3	18.9	15.7
Bolivia, 2002	1.2	24.6	10.0
Cambodia, 1999	15.1	43.8	39.6
Ethiopia, 2000	6.3	27.3	23.1
Ghana, 1998	13.8	43.5	32.6
Guatemala, 2000	3.5	15.2	10.1
Madagascar, 2001	14.4	59.2	50.8
Malawi, 2004	7.8	12.4	11.8
Pakistan, 2001	2.8	27.5	20.3
Peru, 2003	2.9	15.5	6.7
Viet Nam, 1998	7.1	50.6	40.1
Zambia, 1998	2.8	29.6	19.1
Maximum	15.1	59.2	50.8
Minimum	1.2	12.4	6.7
Unweighted average	6.8	30.7	23.3

Source: FAO, 2008a.

FAO's analysis of the welfare impacts of staple food price increases also indicated that female-headed households in most urban, rural and national samples typically fare worse than male-headed households, in that they face either greater welfare losses or smaller welfare gains. This strong result emerged even though female-headed households are not systematically overrepresented among the poor in all, or even most, of the countries. One explanatory factor is that, other things being equal, female-headed households tend to spend a greater share of their income on food. Moreover, in rural contexts, they generally have less access to land and participate less in agricultural income-generating activities and thus cannot share in the benefits of food price increases (FAO, 2008a).

While higher food prices will tend to have a negative impact on the purchasing power of the rural poor, there is also the potential for benefits to this group as a result of increased demand for agricultural labour,

which is a prime source of income for the poor. Indeed, poor and landless families typically rely disproportionately on unskilled wage labour for their income (World Bank, 2007). Higher agricultural prices, by stimulating the demand for unskilled labour in rural areas, can lead to a long-run increase in rural wages, thereby benefiting wage-labour households as well as self-employed farmers. Ravallion (1990), using a dynamic econometric model of wage determination and data from the 1950s to the 1970s, concluded that the average poor landless household in Bangladesh loses in the short run from an increase in rice prices (because of higher consumption expenditures) but gains slightly in the longer run (after five years or more). Indeed, in the long run, as wages adjust, the increase in household income (dominated by unskilled wage labour) becomes large enough to exceed the increase in household expenditures on rice. However, this study used relatively old data, compiled when rice

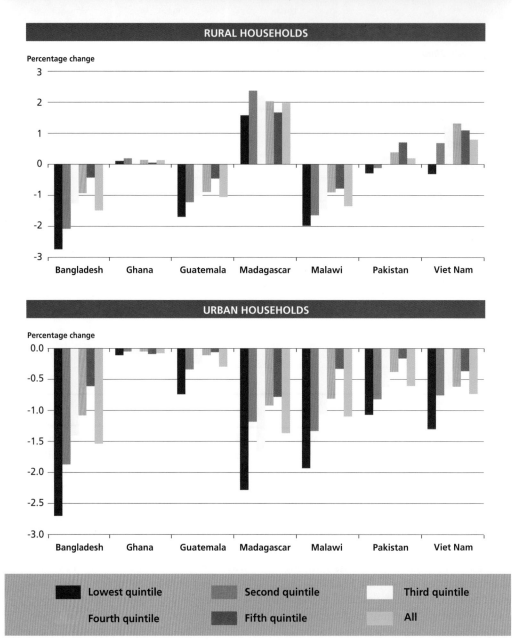

FIGURE 29
Average welfare gain/loss from a 10 percent increase in the price of the main staple, by income (expenditure) quintile for rural and urban households

Source: FAO, 2008a.

farming was a larger sector of the economy and thus had a more profound impact on labour markets. Rashid (2002) found that rice prices in Bangladesh ceased to have a significant effect on agricultural wages after the mid-1970s. If higher rice prices no longer induce higher rural wages in Bangladesh, where agriculture represents a larger

share of the economy and rice dominates the agriculture sector to a greater extent than in most other Asian countries, it seems unlikely that higher cereal prices will provide a significant stimulus to the rural labour market in economies with a more diversified range of employment opportunities.

Higher food prices may also have second-round multiplier effects, as the higher incomes of farmers create demand for other goods and services, many of which will be locally produced. However, if this additional income simply represents a transfer from the rural landless and urban poor, these new multiplier effects will be counterbalanced by negative multiplier effects generated by the reduced incomes of the poor, who will have less money to spend on non-food items as their food bills increase. The net multiplier effects will depend on the change in income distribution and the different spending patterns of the winners and losers from the new set of relative prices.

On balance, at the global level, the immediate net effect of higher food prices on food security is likely to be negative. For example, Senauer and Sur (2001) estimated that a 20 percent increase in food prices in 2025 relative to a baseline will lead to an increase of 440 million in the number of undernourished people in the world (195 million of whom live in sub-Saharan Africa and 158 million in South and East Asia). The International Food Policy Research Institute (IFPRI) estimated that biofuel expansion based on actual national expansion plans would raise the prices of maize, oilseeds, cassava and wheat by 26, 18, 11 and 8 percent, respectively, leading to a decrease in calorie intake of between 2 and 5 percent and an increase in child malnutrition of 4 percent, on average (Msangi, 2008). These, however, are global figures, and the outcome will vary across countries and regions within countries.

Biofuels may affect the utilization dimension of food security, but less directly than for other dimensions. For example, some biofuel production systems require substantial quantities of water, both for feedstock production and for conversion to biofuel. This demand could reduce the availability of water for household use, threatening the health status and thus the food-security status of affected individuals. On the other hand, if bioenergy replaces more polluting energy sources or expands the availability of energy services to the rural poor, it could make cooking both cheaper and cleaner, with positive implications for health status and food utilization.

Biofuel crop production as an impetus for agricultural growth

Biofuels and agriculture as engines of growth

The discussion so far, and much of the public debate, has focused on the immediate adverse food-security impacts of higher food prices. Over the medium-to-longer term, however, there could be a positive supply response not only from smallholders who are net sellers but also from those on the margin and those who are net buyers who are able to react to the price incentives. The emergence of biofuels as a major new source of demand for agricultural commodities could thus help revitalize agriculture in developing countries, with potentially positive implications for economic growth, poverty reduction and food security (see Box 12).

Many of the world's poorest countries are well placed, in agro-ecological terms, to become major producers of biomass for liquid biofuel production – or to respond in general to higher agricultural prices. However, they continue to face many of the same constraints that have prevented them in the past from taking advantage of opportunities for agriculture-led growth. Their ability to take advantage of the new opportunities offered by biofuels – either directly as biofuel feedstock producers or indirectly as producers of agricultural commodities for which prices have gone up – will depend on how these old constraints (and a few new ones) are addressed.

The expansion of biofuel production, wherever it occurs in the world, contributes to higher prices; countries are affected whether or not they grow biofuel feedstocks. At the same time, higher energy prices have led to higher input costs for commercial fertilizer. Increased farm productivity will be fundamental in preventing long-term increases in food prices and excessive pressure for expansion of cultivated area, together with the associated negative environmental effects (including increased greenhouse gas emissions). While, historically, on-farm innovations helped drive productivity gains in Europe and the United States of America, the considerable

BOX 12
Agricultural growth and poverty reduction

Agriculture, due to its size and its linkages
with the rest of the economy – which
remain strong and significant in many of
today's developing countries – has long
been seen by agricultural economists as an
engine of growth in the earlier stages of
development (see, for example, Johnston
and Mellor, 1961; Hazell and Haggblade,
1993). Starting with Ahluwalia's (1978)
work on India, many studies have
attempted to quantify the impact of
agricultural growth on poverty. Seminal
work by Ravallion and Datt (1996) and
Datt and Ravallion (1998) showed that
rural growth, stimulated by agricultural
growth, not only reduced poverty but also
had a stronger effect on poverty reduction
than growth in other sectors such as
manufacturing and services. Furthermore,
rural growth had a significant poverty-
reduction impact also in urban areas.

Cross-country econometric evidence
indicates that GDP growth generated in
agriculture is at least twice as effective
in reducing poverty as growth generated
by other sectors, controlling for the
sector's size (World Bank, 2007). Even in
studies that do not find agriculture to be
the sector contributing most to poverty
reduction, growth in the primary sector
is still found to have a sizeable impact on
the living standards of the poor – well
beyond that suggested by its role in the
economy (Timmer, 2002; Bravo-Ortega and
Lederman, 2005).

The extent to which agricultural
growth contributes to poverty reduction,
depends, however, on the degree of
inequality in a country (Timmer, 2002)

and on the share of agriculture in the
economy and in employment. Most
agricultural growth, over the long term,
stems from technical change (Timmer,
1988). A vast body of literature on the
Green Revolution illustrates the strong
poverty-reducing impact of productivity-
enhancing technological innovation.
Such innovation in agriculture has lifted
millions of people out of poverty by
generating rural income opportunities –
not only for farmers, but also for farm
labourers and other rural providers of
goods and services – and by reducing
prices for consumers (FAO, 2004c). Studies
on China and India have shown that,
dollar for dollar, agricultural research has
historically been one of the most effective
means for poverty reduction through
government spending (Fan, Zhang and
Zhang, 2000; Fan, 2002). Subsequent work
in Uganda has shown similar results (Fan,
Zhang and Rao, 2004).

An FAO study on the roles of agriculture
outlined four main channels through
which agricultural growth can alleviate
poverty (FAO, 2004d; FAO, 2007d): (i) by
directly raising incomes; (ii) by reducing
food prices; (iii) by raising employment;
and (iv) through higher real wages. For
the first of these channels, the distribution
of land is important: a more equitable
land distribution provides a more equal
distribution of the benefits of agricultural
growth (Lopez, 2007). Similarly, the wage
and employment channels are more
effective when urban and rural labour
markets are better integrated (Anríquez
and López, 2007).

resources required to carry out research
on modern agricultural technology means
that publicly funded research is essential.
Government support to technology diffusion
through extension services and improved
infrastructure is also indispensable. Biofuels
strengthen the case for considerably
enhanced investments in agricultural
productivity growth in developing
countries.

**Biofuels, commercialization and
agriculture-sector growth**
Crops cultivated for biofuels, at least from
the farmer's perspective, are no different
from other commercial crops and can be
instrumental in transforming agriculture
from semi-subsistence, low-input and
low-productivity farming systems, which
characterize many parts of the developing
world. Experience has shown that cash-crop

BOX 13
Cotton in the Sahel

Over the past 50 years, and particularly in the past two decades, cotton has become a key export crop for many Sahelian countries. Although cotton is a plantation crop in the European Union and the United States of America, in the Sahel it is grown almost exclusively on small farms. Moreover, this success has not been achieved at the expense of foregone cereal production. Cotton production has contributed to higher incomes, improved livelihoods and better access to social services such as education and health.

Mali is one of the largest cotton producers in the region, and indeed in all of sub-Saharan Africa. In 2006, roughly 200 000 Malian smallholder farmers produced cotton for sale on the international market. Over the past 45 years, cotton production has increased by more than 8 percent per year, providing an average income of US$200 per household for over 25 percent of Malian rural households.

Mali's cotton farmers traditionally cultivate cotton in rotation with coarse grains, particularly maize and sorghum. Contrary to popular fears that cash crops may have a negative effect on food-crop production and household food security, cotton production has actually boosted coarse grain production in Mali. Unlike coarse grains produced outside the cotton zone, cereals grown by cotton farmers benefit from greater access to fertilizer and from the residual effects of cotton fertilizers procured and financed through the region's cotton-based input/credit system. Cereal fields also benefit from improved farming practices made possible through the use of animal traction equipment financed by cotton income. Farmers with animal traction equipment

obtain higher yields in both cotton and coarse grains than the semi-equipped and manual producers (Dioné, 1989; Raymond and Fok 1995; Kébé, Diakite and Diawara, 1998). Well-equipped cotton farmers, likewise, are more able to satisfy the demanding husbandry requirements of maize production, including timely planting, frequent ploughing and regular weeding (Boughton and de Frahan, 1994). They also tend to sell more cereals to the markets. In general, farmers using animal traction account for the majority of cereal sales, primarily because of their higher per capita production.

Historically, an important factor in the success of cotton farmers with both cotton and cereals has been the extension support provided by the Compagnie Malienne de Développement des Textiles (CMDT). The CMDT's construction and maintenance of regional feeder roads has also facilitated the collection and transport of seed cotton. This benefits food-crop marketing by helping to lower marketing costs and improve market integration in the zone. The Malian cotton experience highlights the importance of investing in agriculture if biofuels are to become an engine of agricultural growth.

Cotton also illustrates the impact of OECD countries' subsidies to production and exports and tariffs on imports of farm-based commodities. Anderson and Valenzuela (2007) estimate that the removal of current distortions affecting cotton markets would boost global economic welfare by US$283 million per year and raise the price of cotton by about 13 percent. Moreover, West African cotton farmer's incomes would rise by 40 percent.

Source: based on Tefft (forthcoming).

development by smallholders need not come at the expense of food-crop production or food security in general (see Box 13), although this has occurred in some instances (Binswanger and von Braun, 1991; von Braun, 1994).

Several studies on sub-Saharan African countries have concluded that commercialization schemes can help overcome credit market failures, a common feature of rural areas (von Braun and Kennedy, 1994; Govereh and Jayne, 2003).

In addition, the introduction of cash crops to a region may stimulate private investment in distribution, retail, market infrastructure and human capital, which ultimately also benefits food-crop production and other farm activities. Where farmers have timely access to credit and inputs, and to extension services and equipment, they are able not only to boost their incomes, but also to intensify food production on their lands. Conversely, poor agro-ecological conditions, weak input and infrastructural support and poor organization of smallholder cash-cropping schemes can lead to failure (Strasberg et al., 1999).

In terms of the employment effects, net job creation is more likely to occur if biofuel feedstock production does not displace other agricultural activities or if the displaced activities are less labour-intensive. The outcome will vary, depending on a country's endowments in land and labour, on the crop used as feedstock and on the crops that were grown previously. Even within a single country and for one individual crop, labour intensity can vary substantially; in Brazil, for example, sugar-cane production uses three times as much labour in the northeast as it does in the centre-south (Kojima and Johnson, 2005).

Research by von Braun and Kennedy (1994) found that the employment effects of commercial crops for poor households were generally significant. In Brazil, the biofuel sector accounted for about 1 million jobs in 2001 (Moreira, 2006). These jobs were in rural areas and mostly for unskilled labour. The indirect creation of employment in manufacturing and other sectors was estimated at about another 300 000 jobs.

Promoting smallholder participation in biofuel crop production

Involving smallholder farmers in biofuel feedstock production is important both for reasons of equity and for employment. Are biofuel crops more likely to be produced on plantations or by small farmers? Hayami (2002) points out that smallholders have certain advantages over plantations in that they can avoid problems related to supervision and monitoring and can be more flexible. Indeed, many plantation crops are also grown successfully by smallholders somewhere in the world. In Thailand, for example, where smallholders are generally prominent in terms of numbers and production, they compare favourably, in efficiency terms, with large- and medium-sized sugar farms in Australia, France and the United States of America (Larson and Borrell, 2001). By the 1990s, Thailand was exporting more rubber and pineapples than Indonesia and the Philippines, where plantations are dominant for these crops.

However, when processing and marketing become more complex and centralized, plantations represent a solution to the need for vertical integration of production with other processes – as is the case for palm oil, tea, bananas and sisal. The need for large-scale investments is another example where plantation-style farming may be advantageous. If investors have to build supporting infrastructure such as irrigation, roads and docking, the scale of the operation necessary to offset the costs will be even larger. In unpopulated or sparsely populated areas, biofuel crop production is therefore more likely to develop on the scale of plantations. This is one key reason why sugar cane in the Philippines is produced by smallholders in old settled areas of Luzon while plantations dominate in areas of Negros that were settled more recently (Hayami, Quisumbing and Adriano, 1990).

Smallholder productivity and profitability are often held back by poorly working commodity markets, lack of access to financial markets, poorly performing producer organizations and significant input market failures, especially for seed and fertilizer in sub-Saharan Africa. Government policy can promote smallholder farming. Key areas for policy intervention are:

- investment in public goods such as infrastructure, irrigation, extension and research;
- the sponsoring of innovative approaches to rural finance;
- the creation of market information systems;
- improvements in output and input markets in rural areas so that small farms are not at a disadvantage relative to larger farms;
- the enforcement of contracts.

Producer organizations that foster collective action can also help reduce transaction costs and achieve market power to the benefit of smallholder competitiveness (World Bank, 2007). The experience of the Green Revolution shows how responsive small-farmer productivity and output supply can be to public investment in research, irrigation and input supply.

At least in the early years, when biofuel crop production is gaining momentum, investors ready to inject the necessary capital are likely to look for some security of supply. One way to achieve this is by establishing a plantation of the crop on which production is based. However, smallholder participation in the form of contract farming (also referred to as "outgrower schemes") is perhaps the most obvious approach to building the necessary market while safeguarding staple-food production and ensuring pro-poor growth. Contract farming implies the availability of credit, timely supply of inputs, knowledge transfer, provision of extension services and access to a ready market. From the contractors' perspective, this type of arrangement can improve acceptability to stakeholders and overcome land constraints.

In many countries, contract farming is encouraged by governments as a means for enabling rural farming households and communities to share in the benefits of commercial agriculture while maintaining some independence (FAO, 2001). Contract/outgrower schemes are more likely to succeed if they are based on proven technology and an enabling policy and legal environment. Default by contract farmers can be a major problem in the operation of such schemes. A weak legal system, weak insurance services and the associated high transaction costs lead to considerable risk for companies (Coulter *et al.*, 1999).

Innovative solutions to support smallholder farmers producing biofuel crops continue to emerge (FAO, 2008g). In Brazil, the government created the Social Fuel Stamp programme to encourage biodiesel producers to purchase feedstocks from small family farms in poorer regions of the country. Companies that join the scheme benefit from partial or total federal tax exemption. By the end of 2007, some 400 000 small farmers had joined the programme, selling mainly palm oil, soybeans and/or castor beans to refining companies.

Biofuel crop development: equity and gender concerns

Important risks associated with the development of biofuels relate to worsening income distribution and a deterioration of women's status. The distributional impact of developing biofuel crops will depend on initial conditions and on government policies. The consensus with regard to the impact of cash crops on inequality appears to lean towards greater inequality (Maxwell and Fernando, 1989). However, evidence from the Green Revolution suggests that adoption was much less uneven than was first supposed. Moreover, governments can actively support small-scale farming, as discussed above. The impact on inequality will depend on the crop and technology employed, with a scale-neutral technology favouring equal distribution of benefits. Other important factors are: the distribution of land with secure ownership or tenancy rights; the degree of access by farmers to input and output markets and to credit; and a level playing field in terms of policies.

Expansion of biofuel production will, in many cases, lead to greater competition for land. For smallholder farmers, women farmers and/or pastoralists, who may have weak land-tenure rights, this could lead to displacement. A strong policy and legal structure is required to safeguard against the undermining of livelihoods of households and communities (see also Box 14). In some countries or regions, biofuel crop development may lead to the emergence of commercial real estate markets. At the same time, land rental values are likely to rise and poor farmers may not be in a position to secure land through buying or renting. Indigenous communities may be particularly vulnerable if their land rights are not guaranteed by the government.

Bouis and Haddad (1994) found that the introduction of sugar cane in the southern Bukidnon province of the Philippines led to a worsening of the land-tenure situation, with many households losing their access to land. The establishment of large sugar

BOX 14
Biofuel crops and the land issue in the United Republic of Tanzania

While the Tanzanian Government is encouraging investors to consider the United Republic of Tanzania for ethanol and biodiesel production, it is also trying to grapple with a number of uncertainties and constraints. First and foremost are the interrelated questions of land availability and food security. Requests for land for bioenergy crops (mainly sugar cane, oil palm and jatropha) are in the order of 50–100 000 hectares at a time. Although there will be a considerable time lag before such large-scale plans are transformed into planted fields – developments currently being implemented are in the 5–25 000 hectare range – the short- to long-term implications for food security are being studied as a matter or urgency.

For many households in the United Republic of Tanzania, their food security depends on access to land. There are concerns that the amount of land being requested cannot be met without displacing households from their land. Because suitable farming land mostly belongs to villages, some argue that no free land is available. Others, however, argue that only a small percentage of cultivable land is actually being used for crop production. Large amounts of land are under the control of government institutions such as the Prisons Service and the National Service, and while village land may indeed be used by farming communities, much unused land remains available according to the Tanzania Investment Centre and the Sugar Board of Tanzania. However, investors are looking for land close to existing infrastructure and reasonably close to ports and are not interested in the vast areas that are not currently serviced by adequate infrastructure. Over the longer term, poor infrastructure, weak extension services, the near-complete lack of credit and low yields are obstacles that will continue to inhibit transformation of the country's agriculture sector.

Access to land is complex in the United Republic of Tanzania. All land is classified as either village land or national land. The procedure for renting village land is both complicated and time-consuming as the potential investor must obtain consent at the village, district, regional and then ministry levels. Presidential consent may even be required, depending on the size of land area requested. At the end of the process, the village land is reclassified as national land with the land deed held by the Tanzania Investment Centre, which then leases the land to the investor for up to 99 years. This process, which involves the payment of compensation to farm households, can take up to two years. Leasing national land is a much shorter process. A more effective mechanism for locating appropriate land, assessing food-security implications and coordinating information flows among the various ministries, agencies and investors involved is needed in order to create the necessary investor-friendly environment while safeguarding the welfare of the affected populations.

In part, the land issue highlights the lack of a bioenergy policy and the legal framework required to support government and investor decisions. Indeed, both investors and government officials frequently state that the absence of bioenergy policy is the single most pressing problem facing the development of the sector.

Sources: based on or informed by the authors' discussions with officials at the Ministry of Agriculture, Food and Cooperatives, Ministry of Energy, Tanzania Investment Centre, Sugar Board of Tanzania, United Nations Industrial Development Organization (UNIDO), United Nations Development Programme (UNDP) and United Nations Children's Fund (UNICEF); with representatives from InfEnergy, Sun Biofuels, British Petroleum, Diligent Energy Systems, SEKAB, Deutsche Gesellschaft für Technische Zusammenarbeit GmbH (GTZ) and Tanzania Traditional Energy Development and Environment Organisation (TaTEDO); and with researchers from the Microbiology Unit at the University of Dar es Salaam.

haciendas without a net increase in demand for labour meant that income inequality also deteriorated. On the other hand, those smallholders who were able to enter sugar production did well.

FAO (2008h) suggests that female farmers may be at a distinct disadvantage *vis-à-vis* male farmers in terms of benefiting from biofuel crop development. To start with, there are often significant gender disparities with regard to access to land, water, credit and other inputs. Although women are often responsible for carrying out much of the agricultural work, in particular in sub-Saharan Africa, they typically own little of the land (UNICEF, 2007). In Cameroon, women provide three-quarters of agricultural labour but own less than 10 percent of the land; in Brazil, they own 11 percent of the land while in Peru they own slightly more than 13 percent. Unequal rights to land create an uneven playing field for men and women, making it more difficult for women and female-headed households to benefit from biofuel crop production (FAO, 2008h).

The emphasis on exploiting marginal lands for biofuel crop production may also work against female farmers. For example, in India, these marginal lands, or so-called "wastelands", are frequently classified as common property resources and are often of crucial importance to the poor. Evidence from India shows that gathering and use of common property resources are largely women's and children's work – a division of labour that is also often found in West Africa (Beck and Nesmith, 2000). However, women are rarely involved in the management of these resources.

In a study by von Braun and Kennedy (1994), it was found that in "none of the case studies they analysed did women play a significant role as decision-makers and operators of the more commercialized crop, even when typical 'women's crops' were promoted". Dey (1981), in her review of rice development projects in the Gambia, also highlighted the importance of incorporating information about women's role in agriculture when designing commercialization schemes so as to generate a better outcome in terms of equity, nutritional outcomes and even overall performance.

As has emerged from the discussion above, the development of biofuel production may bring to the forefront a series of equity- and gender-related issues, such as labour conditions on plantations, constraints faced by smallholders and the disadvantaged position of female farmers. These are critical and fundamental issues that largely derive from existing institutional and political realities in many countries and that must be addressed in parallel with the prospects for biofuel development in a specific context. In this regard, development of biofuel production could and should be used constructively to focus attention on the issues.

Key messages of the chapter

- Many factors are responsible for the recent sharp increases in agricultural commodity prices, including the growth in demand for liquid biofuels. Biofuels will continue to exert upward pressure on commodity prices, which will have implications for food security and poverty levels in developing countries.
- At the country level, higher commodity prices will have negative consequences for net food-importing developing countries. Especially for the low-income food-deficit countries, higher import prices can severely strain their food import bills.
- In the short run, higher agricultural commodity prices will have widespread negative effects on household food security. Particularly at risk are poor urban consumers and poor net food buyers in rural areas, who tend also to be the majority of the rural poor. There is a strong need for establishing appropriate safety nets to ensure access to food by the poor and vulnerable.
- In the longer run, growing demand for biofuels and the resulting rise in agricultural commodity prices can present an opportunity for promoting agricultural growth and rural development in developing countries. They strengthen the case for focusing on agriculture as an engine of growth for poverty alleviation. This requires strong government commitment to enhancing

agricultural productivity, for which public investments are crucial. Support must focus particularly on enabling poor small producers to expand their production and gain access to markets.

- Production of biofuel feedstocks may offer income-generating opportunities for farmers in developing countries. Experience shows that cash-crop production for markets does not necessarily come at the expense of food crops and that it may contribute to improving food security.
- Promoting smallholder participation in biofuel crop production requires active government policies and support. Crucial areas are investment in public goods (infrastructure, research extension, etc.), rural finance, market information, market institutions and legal systems.
- In many cases, private investors interested in developing biofuel feedstock production in developing countries will look to the establishment of plantations to ensure security of

supply. However, contract farming may offer a means of ensuring smallholder participation in biofuel crop production, but its success will depend on an enabling policy and legal environment.

- Development of biofuel feedstock production may present equity- and gender-related risks concerning issues such as labour conditions on plantations, access to land, constraints faced by smallholders and the disadvantaged position of women. Generally, these risks derive from existing institutional and political realities in the countries and call for attention irrespective of developments related to biofuels.
- Governments need to establish clear criteria for determining "productive use" requirements and legal definitions for what constitutes "idle" land. Effective application of land-tenure policies that aim to protect vulnerable communities is no less important.

7. Policy challenges

Liquid biofuels for transport have been the subject of considerable debate concerning their potential to contribute to climate-change mitigation and energy security, while also helping to promote development in rural areas. However, as some of the initial assumptions concerning biofuels have come under closer scrutiny, it has become increasingly clear that biofuels also raise a series of critical questions concerning their economic, environmental and social impacts. Biofuels present both opportunities and risks from an environmental and social perspective. Developing socially and environmentally sustainable biofuel production that exploits the opportunities, while managing or minimizing the risks, will depend crucially on the policies pursued vis-à-vis the sector.

The preceding chapters have reviewed the role of biofuels – both actual and potential – and the main challenges and issues involved in their development from economic, environmental, poverty and food-security perspectives. A series of the most critical questions surrounding biofuels have been addressed and an attempt made to provide answers based on the evidence available to date. This chapter tries to spell out what are the implications for the design of appropriate policies for the sector.

■
Questions addressed by the report

The key questions addressed by the report and the answers provided can be summarized as follows.

■ *Do biofuels threaten food security?*
For poor net buyers of food staples in both urban and rural areas, higher food prices resulting in part from increased biofuel demand will pose an immediate threat to their food security. Even if biofuels are only one of several sources of the recent sharp increases in food prices, expanded biofuel production can still continue to exert upward pressure on food prices for considerable time

to come. The immediate impact of high food prices on the poor can be mitigated through appropriately designed and targeted safety nets that support access to food. At the same time, it is important to allow rising prices to feed through to farmers so as to trigger a possible supply response. Imposing price controls and export bans, as many countries have done in 2008 in efforts to protect consumers from high prices, prevents markets from adjusting and, while providing an apparent short-term relief, may actually prolong and deepen the food-security crisis. If markets are allowed to function and price signals are effectively transmitted to producers, higher prices will provide an incentive for increased production and increased employment, which may alleviate food-security concerns over the longer term.

■ *Can biofuels help promote agricultural development?*
Although higher prices for agricultural commodities constitute an immediate threat to food security for poor consumers worldwide, in the longer run they represent an opportunity for agricultural development. This opportunity can be realized only when and where the agriculture sector has the capacity to respond to the price incentives and poor farmers, in particular, are able to participate in the supply response. Expanding demand for biofuels may reverse the long-term decline in real agricultural commodity prices that, for decades, has discouraged public and private investment in agriculture and rural areas in many developing countries. These countries may be able to use this opportunity to revitalize their agriculture sectors, but, as for agriculture in general, their ability to do this will depend on investments in infrastructure, institutions and technology, among other factors. Promoting access to productive resources, particularly by smallholders and marginalized groups such as women and minorities, will strongly improve the likelihood that agriculture can serve as an engine of growth and poverty reduction. Opportunities would also be

expanded by the removal of subsidies and trade barriers that benefit producers in OECD countries at the expense of producers in developing countries.

■ *Can biofuels help reduce greenhouse gas emissions?*

Some biofuels may, under certain conditions, help reduce greenhouse gas emissions. In practice, however, the global effects of an expansion of biofuel production will depend crucially on where and how the feedstocks are produced. Land-use change resulting from increased feedstock production is a key determining factor. For many locations, emissions from land-use change – whether direct or indirect – are likely to exceed, or at least offset, much of the greenhouse gas savings obtained by using biofuels for transport. Moreover, even when biofuels are effective in reducing greenhouse gas emissions, they may not be the most cost-effective way of achieving this objective compared with other options. Good agricultural practices and increased yields can help mitigate some of the negative greenhouse gas effects arising from land-use change, and technological developments and improvements in infrastructure, leading to increased yields per hectare, can contribute to a more favourable outcome. Second-generation technologies, in particular, may improve the greenhouse gas balance of biofuel production significantly.

■ *Do biofuels threaten land, water and biodiversity?*

As for any form of agriculture, expanded biofuel production may threaten land and water resources as well as biodiversity, and appropriate policy measures are required to minimize possible negative effects. The impacts will vary across feedstocks and locations and will depend on cultivation practices and whether new land is converted for production of biofuel feedstocks or other crops are displaced by biofuels. Expanded demand for agricultural commodities will exacerbate pressures on the natural resource base, especially if the demand is met through area expansion. On the other hand, the use of perennial feedstocks on marginal or degraded lands may offer promise for sustainable biofuel production, but the economic viability of such options may be a constraint at least in the short run.

■ *Can biofuels help achieve energy security?*

Liquid biofuels based on agricultural crops can only be expected to make a limited contribution to global supply of transport fuels and a yet smaller contribution to total energy supplies. Because agricultural markets are small relative to energy markets, expanding biofuel production quickly bids up the price of agricultural feedstocks and makes them uncompetitive against petroleum-based fuels. However, countries with a large natural-resource base that can produce feedstocks competitively and process them efficiently may be able to develop an economically viable biofuel sector. Unforeseen changes in energy markets could also change the economic viability of biofuels. Technological innovation – including the development of second-generation biofuels based on cellulosic feedstocks – may expand the potential and the range of countries where biofuels could make a significant contribution to energy security. However, it is not clear when second-generation technologies may become commercially viable. When they do, first- and second-generation fuels are likely to continue to coexist; the bulk of biofuel supply will be provided by first-generation biofuels, based on sugar, starchy and oil crops at least for a decade.

A framework for better biofuel policies

Liquid biofuels for transport have been actively promoted, especially by some OECD countries, through a series of policies providing incentives and support for their production and use. Such policies have been largely driven by national and domestic agendas. A strong driver has been the desire to support farmers and rural communities. They have also been based on assumptions about the positive contribution of biofuels to energy security and climate-change mitigation that are increasingly being challenged. The unintended consequences, especially in terms of market and food-security impacts, have frequently been overlooked. It is increasingly recognized that a more consistent set of policies and approaches towards biofuels is needed, based on a clearer understanding of their implications that are now emerging.

Policies must be aimed at grasping the potential opportunities offered by biofuels, while carefully managing the indisputable risks they also present. They must be consistent with policies in other related areas and based on clear and sound policy principles if they are to be effective. Unfortunately, these policies must also be formulated in a situation of considerable uncertainty.

Uncertainties, opportunities and risks

Policy-making for biofuels has to take into account the high degree of uncertainty still surrounding the potential and future role of liquid biofuels in global energy supplies. This uncertainty is underscored by the considerable variation in estimates of the potential for bioenergy supply in the medium-to-long term presented in various recent studies. However, in general, the studies suggest that land requirements would be too large to allow liquid biofuels to displace fossil fuels on a large scale. The development of biofuels must be seen as part of a long-term process of moving towards a world that is less reliant on fossil fuels, in which biofuels represent one of several renewable energy sources. However, even if the contribution of biofuels to global energy supply remains small, it may still imply a considerable impact on agriculture and food security.

Foremost among the factors contributing to uncertainty are future trends in fossil fuel prices, which will determine the economic viability of liquid biofuels. In the medium-to-long term, technology developments in the field of biofuels may alter the underlying equations determining their profitability. Such developments may be in the areas of feedstock production technologies (e.g. agronomic developments) and conversion technologies. Moving towards second-generation biofuels based on lignocellulosic feedstocks may significantly change the prospects for, and characteristics of, biofuel development and expand its potential. Technology and policy developments in other areas of renewable energy and in the field of energy conservation will also have an impact,

as will overall developments in global and national energy policies and in policies addressing climate-change mitigation.

Biofuels have been seen as offering opportunities both from an economic and social and from an environmental and natural resource perspective. However, also these dimensions are surrounded by considerable uncertainty, and their actual magnitude is not clear. The socio-economic opportunities derive from an increase in demand for farm output, which could boost rural incomes and stimulate rural development. From the environmental and natural resource perspective, there have been expectations that biofuels may, under appropriate conditions, contribute to reducing greenhouse gas emissions. Other expected benefits have included reductions in emissions of regulated air pollutants from combustion engines and the potential for biomass feedstocks to contribute to restoring degraded lands.

Greater attention is now being paid to the risks involved in biofuel development. The risks, which have been documented by this report, are both socio-economic and environmental. The socio-economic risks are largely associated with the negative implications on poor and vulnerable net food buyers of higher food prices resulting from increased demand for agricultural commodities. The increased competition for resources – land and water – may also pose threats to poor unempowered rural dwellers who lack tenure security, with women often among the most vulnerable. From the environmental perspective, it is becoming clear that greenhouse gas emission reductions are far from a guaranteed outcome of substituting biofuels for fossil fuels. The impact depends on how biofuels are produced – both in terms of how crops are grown and of how conversion takes place – as well as on how they are brought to the market. The global impact is more likely to be negative if large tracts of additional land are brought under agricultural cultivation.

Policy coherence

Biofuel developments are shaped by several different policy domains – agriculture, energy, transport, environment and trade – often without clear coordination and coherence among the policies pursued in each. Only if the role of biofuels is considered in relation to each of these policy domains can it be ensured that they play the appropriate role in reaching the various policy objectives.

For example, biofuels currently rely on many of the same agricultural commodities that are destined for food use. Their feedstocks compete with conventional agriculture for land and other productive resources; food and agriculture policy is therefore central to biofuel policy development. At the same time, biofuels are only one among many possible sources of renewable energy, a field where technological innovation is moving rapidly; therefore biofuel policy must be considered within the wider context of energy policy. Similarly, biofuels only constitute one option for reducing greenhouse gas emissions, and so must be evaluated against alternative mitigation strategies. Choices in the field of transport policies also crucially affect the demand for liquid biofuels. Finally, trade policies can support or hinder the development of environmentally sustainable biofuels. If trade barriers prevent the most efficient and most sustainable geographic pattern of biofuel production and trade, they may undermine the environmental objectives of biofuels.

Policy principles
Five guiding principles are proposed for effective policy approaches to biofuels.

- Biofuel policies must be protective of the poor and food-insecure. Priority should be given to the problems posed by higher food prices for the food-importing countries, especially among the least-developed countries, and the poor and vulnerable net food buyers in rural and urban areas. Potential opportunities to improve food security and the rural economy offered by biofuel developments should be exploited.
- They should be growth-enabling, both by improving economic and technical efficiency and by ensuring that developing countries can participate in future market opportunities. Policies should therefore promote research and development, thereby enhancing the efficiency, as well as environmental

sustainability, of feedstock production and biofuel conversion processes. Similarly, they should create an enabling environment to support a broad-based supply response to biofuel demand in developing countries, allowing poor farmers the possibility of reaping the benefits.
- Biofuel policies should be environmentally sustainable. They should strive to ensure that biofuels make a strong positive contribution to reducing greenhouse gas emissions, protect land and water resources from depletion and environmental damage and prevent excessive new loadings of pollutants.
- They should be outward-looking and market-oriented so as to reduce existing distortions in biofuel and agricultural markets and avoid introducing new ones. They should also be based on a consideration of unintended consequences that may go beyond national borders.
- Policies should be developed with appropriate international coordination to ensure that the international system supports environmental sustainability goals as well as social goals for agricultural development and poverty and hunger reduction.

Areas for policy action

The following section reviews some of the main policy issues to be addressed in order to ensure the environmentally and socially sustainable development of the biofuels sector. Some of the issues raised are specific to biofuels. Others are well-known issues that relate to sustainable agricultural development and food security in general, but that are gaining increased importance by the emergence of biofuels as a new source of demand for agricultural commodities.

Protecting the poor and food-insecure
As has been emphasized, biofuel policies are not the only reason behind the recent increase in commodity prices. Nevertheless, growing demand for biofuels has certainly contributed to the upward pressure on agricultural and food prices and could continue to do so for some time to come,

even if and when some of the other factors underlying the current high prices subside. The magnitude of the effect is uncertain and will depend on the pace of development of the sector and on the policies relating to biofuel development pursued in both developed and developing countries. However, there is a clear need to address the negative food-security implications for net food-importing developing countries (especially the least-developed countries) and poor net food-buying households, even beyond the current emergency situation of widespread and severe threats to food security.

An important step forward would be for countries to refrain from pursuing and adopting policies that put a premium on and promote demand for biofuel feedstocks to the detriment of food supplies, as is the case for the current widely applied mandates and subsidies supporting biofuel production and consumption.

Safety nets are required to protect poor and vulnerable net food buyers from nutritional deprivation and reductions in their real purchasing power. In the immediate context of rapidly rising food prices, protecting the most vulnerable may require direct food distribution, targeted food subsidies and cash transfers, and nutritional programmes such as school feeding. Import and generalized subsidies may also be required. In the short-to-medium run, social protection programmes must be established, or expanded and strengthened. Well-organized and targeted social protection systems are potentially capable of providing direct support to the neediest at a substantially lower cost than that of more broad-based actions; this, in turn, makes them more sustainable.

In the medium-to-long run, the impact of higher food prices could be mitigated by a supply response from the agriculture sector. Such a response would require effective transmission of prices to the farmgate. Effective price transmission is dependent both on policy and on the existence of adequate institutional and physical infrastructure to support effective markets. Policy interventions to control prices or disrupt trade flows, while providing an apparent immediate relief, may be counterproductive in the longer run, because they interfere with price incentives to producers. Investment in infrastructure for storage and transportation is also crucial for the effective functioning of markets.

Taking advantage of opportunities for agricultural and rural development

While representing an immediate threat to the food security of poor and vulnerable net food buyers, higher prices for agricultural commodities induced by growing demand for biofuels can present long-term opportunities for agricultural and rural development, income generation and employment. They can constitute an important element in the effort to re-launch agriculture by providing incentives to the private sector to invest and produce. However, higher prices alone will not generate broad-based agricultural development; investments in productivity increases in developing countries will be an indispensable complement. Productivity increases will require significant and sustained improvements in long-neglected areas such as research, extension, and agricultural and general infrastructure, along with credit and risk-management instruments – all of which must complement improved price incentives.

Efforts need to focus particularly on enabling poor rural producers – those who are least able to respond to changing market signals – to expand their production and marketed supply. Agricultural research must address the needs of such poor producers, many of whom farm in increasingly marginal areas. It is also crucial to enhance their access to agricultural services, including extension, and financial services, and to strengthen their capacity to take advantage of these services. No less fundamental is securing their access to natural resources such as land and water and fostering their participation in non-agricultural sources of income, including payment schemes for environmental services. Land-policy issues are critical, especially the need to ensure that the land rights of vulnerable and disadvantaged communities are respected. Support to poor rural households is needed, to help them strengthen their livelihoods in conditions of ever greater climatic uncertainty, and allow them to benefit from new approaches to managing weather and other risks, including new forms of insurance.

Ensuring environmental sustainability
It must be ensured that further expansion of biofuel production will provide a positive contribution to climate-change mitigation. For this purpose, there is a critical need for an improved understanding of the effects of biofuels on land-use change, which is the source of the most significant effects on greenhouse gas emissions. Other negative environmental impacts must also be assessed and minimized. Harmonized approaches to life-cycle analysis, greenhouse gas balances and criteria for sustainable production should be developed in order to ensure consistency in approach.

Support to biofuels has generated an artificially rapid growth in biofuel production. Reducing the rate of expansion by eliminating subsidies and mandates for biofuel production and consumption will help improve environmental sustainability, as it will allow time for improved technologies and yield increases to become effective and thus ease the pressure for expansion of cultivated areas. Research and development, as well as investing in productivity increases, may help reduce the stress on the natural resource base caused by expanded biofuel production. Indeed, improved technologies, both in feedstock production and conversion to biofuels, will be crucial for ensuring long-term sustainability of biofuel production.

Sustainability criteria and relative certification can help ensure environmental sustainability, although they cannot directly address the effects of land-use change resulting from an increased scale of production. However, criteria must be carefully assessed; they must apply only to global public goods and must be designed so as to avoid creating additional trade barriers and imposing undue constraints on the development potential of developing countries. The issue of possible differential treatment of biofuel feedstocks and agricultural products in general must be addressed and clarified. There is no intrinsic justification for treating the two differently – nor may a distinction be feasible in practice.

As for any type of agricultural production, promotion of good agricultural practices may constitute a practical approach to reducing the negative effects, in terms of climate change and other environmental impacts, of expanded biofuel production. Payments for environmental services provided by feedstock producers through sustainable production are also an instrument that can be used in conjunction with sustainability criteria to encourage sustainable production. Initially, the promotion of good practices could be combined with capacity building for the countries in greatest need. In time, more stringent standards and certification systems could be gradually introduced.

Reviewing existing biofuel policies
OECD countries, in particular, have been providing significant levels of support to the biofuel sector, without which most of their biofuel production is unlikely to have been economically viable given existing technologies and recent relative prices of commodity feedstocks and crude oil. The main policy objectives, apart from support to farm incomes, have been climate-change mitigation and energy security. The policies adopted have focused on mandates and significant subsidies to production and consumption of liquid biofuels. Trade protection measures, such as tariffs, have limited market access for potential developing-country producers of biofuels, to the detriment of an efficient international pattern of production and resource allocation. Such support and protection have been added to the already extremely high levels of subsidies and protection to the agriculture sector that have characterized agricultural policies in most OECD countries for decades and have exacerbated the market-distorting effects of these policies.

There is an urgent need to review these biofuel policies in the light of emerging knowledge about biofuels and their implications. Such a review should be based on an assessment of their effectiveness in reaching their objectives and of their costs. The evidence discussed in this report indicates that the policies pursued have not been effective in achieving energy security and climate-change mitigation. Indeed, in terms of energy security, biofuels will be able to contribute only a small portion of global energy supply. The assumed mitigation of greenhouse gas emissions is also not certain; it appears that rapid expansion of biofuel production may increase rather than reduce emissions, especially where large-scale land-use change is involved. The policies pursued have been costly to the OECD countries, and the costs may escalate as production levels expand. Based on current knowledge, the arguments seem weak for maintaining some of the current policies such as blending mandates, subsidies to production and consumption, and trade barriers for biofuels. Expenditures on biofuels would be much better directed towards research and development – both for agriculture in general and biofuels more specifically – aimed at improving economic and technical efficiency, and sustainability, rather than towards subsidies linked to production and consumption. Moving towards second-generation biofuels, in particular, would appear to hold significant promise.

Political economy considerations also speak against the subsidies for biofuels. Even where subsidies could be justified (e.g. based on infant industry arguments) and are intended to be only temporary, experience (e.g. earlier agricultural policies) shows that subsidies are extremely difficult to eliminate once they have become entrenched.

Policy coherence is also a critical issue. Biofuels are only one among many sources of renewable energy and only represent one among a range of alternative strategies for greenhouse gas mitigation. With regard to energy security, it is important to ensure equal conditions for different sources and suppliers of renewable energy, at the national and international levels, and to avoid promoting biofuels over other sources. In the case of greenhouse gas mitigation, carbon taxes and tradable permits constitute mechanisms that place a cost or price on carbon and thereby stimulate the most efficient carbon-reduction response, which may involve energy conservation, biofuels and other technologies.

Abolishing the current mandates and subsidies linked to production and consumption would bring other benefits or minimize some of the negative implications of biofuels. Subsidies and mandates have created an artificially rapid growth in biofuel production, exacerbating some of its negative effects. This policy-induced rapid growth has placed significant upward pressure on food prices and is one of the factors (although perhaps not the most important one) contributing to the recent rapid increase. It is also intensifying the

pressures on the natural resource base through its effects on land-use change. As emphasized above, more gradual development of the sector would ease the upward pressure on prices and reduce the stress on natural resources, as technologies could be developed and disseminated, allowing a larger share of the demand to be met through sustainable yield increases rather than area expansion.

Enhancing international system support to sustainable biofuel development

International trade rules and national trade policies for agriculture and biofuels should be made more conducive to an efficient and equitable international allocation of resources. The current combination of subsidies, mandates and trade barriers does not serve this purpose. Biofuel trade policies should enhance opportunities for agricultural producers and biofuel processors in developing countries, in line with their comparative advantage, by eliminating existing trade barriers. This will contribute to a more efficient pattern of biofuel production at the international level.

There is a need for an appropriate international forum in which sustainability criteria can be debated and agreed so as to ensure that they achieve their intended environmental objectives without creating unnecessary barriers to developing-country suppliers. It is also important to ensure that sustainability criteria and related certification schemes are not introduced unilaterally and do not constitute an additional barrier to trade. To the extent that sustainability criteria are established, the international community has an obligation to provide assistance in capacity building to developing countries.

The international donor community, likewise, has a clear responsibility to support developing countries in addressing the immediate threats to their food security, resulting from higher food prices, by contributing resources for the necessary measures to assist and protect the most vulnerable and negatively affected countries and population groups.

International donors must also recognize the opportunities arising from biofuel development and redouble their support to agricultural development. Many of the opportunities and challenges associated with biofuels are the same as those already experienced with agricultural expansion and intensification. However, the expansion of biofuels and the ensuing price increases for agricultural products increase the returns on agricultural investments and strengthen the case for enhanced development assistance aimed especially at the agriculture sector.

Conclusions

Production and consumption of biofuels have increased dramatically in the past few years, driven largely by policies aimed at enhancing energy security, reducing greenhouse gas emissions and supporting agricultural development. This rapid growth has in many ways outpaced our understanding of the potential impacts on food security and the environment. As our recognition of emerging impacts grows, the need arises to put biofuel policies on a more solid base. The challenge we face is that of reducing the risks posed by biofuels while at the same time ensuring that the opportunities they present are shared more widely. There is an urgent need to review existing biofuel policies in an international context in order to protect the poor and food-insecure and to promote broad-based rural and agricultural development while ensuring environmental sustainability.

Views from civil society

Agrofuels or food sovereignty?

From the International Planning Committee for Food Sovereignty (IPC)

www.foodsovereignty.org

The current massive wave of investment in energy production based on the cultivation and industrial processing of crops like maize, soy, palm oil, sugar cane, canola, etc., will not solve the climate crisis nor the energy crisis. It will bring disastrous social and environmental consequences. It is already one of the causes behind the current food crisis. It creates a new and very serious threat to food production by small farmers and to the attainment of food sovereignty for the world population.

It is claimed that agrofuels will help fight climate change. In reality, the opposite is true. The new extensive monoculture plantations for the production of agrofuels are increasing greenhouse gases through deforestation, drainage of wetlands, and dismantling of communal lands. There is simply not enough land in the world to generate all the fuel necessary for an industrial society whose needs for transport of people and goods are continually increasing. The promise of agrofuels creates the illusion that we can continue to consume energy at an ever-growing rate. The only answer to the threat of climate change is to reduce energy use worldwide, and to redirect international trade towards local markets.

To address climate change, we don't need agrofuel plantations to produce fuel energy. Instead, we need to turn the industrial food system upside down. We need policies and strategies to reduce the consumption of energy and to prevent waste. Such policies and strategies already exist and are being fought for. In agriculture and food production, they mean orienting production towards local rather than international markets; they mean adopting strategies to keep people on the land, rather than throwing them off; they mean supporting sustained and sustainable approaches for bringing biodiversity back into agriculture; they mean diversifying agricultural production systems, using and expanding on local knowledge; and they mean putting local communities back in the driving seat of rural development. Or put simply: it means a resolute move towards food sovereignty!

We demand:

- The end of corporate-driven, monoculture-based production of agrofuels. As a first step, a five-year international moratorium on the production, trade and consumption of industrial agrofuels has to be immediately declared.
- An in-depth evaluation of the social and environment costs of the agrofuel boom and of profits made by transnational corporations in the processing and trade of the raw materials.
- The promotion and development of small-scale production and local consumption models and the rejection of consumerism.
- Explicit support from governments and institutions to the sustainable peasant-based model of food production and distribution, with its minimal use of energy, its capacity to create jobs, to respect cultural and biological diversity and its positive effect on global warming (fertile soils are the best way to capture CO_2).
- The reorientation of agricultural policies towards sustainable rural communities and livelihoods based on food sovereignty and genuine agrarian reform.

Biofuels: a new opportunity for family agriculture

From the International Federation of Agricultural Producers (IFAP)

www.ifap.org

The production of food and feed remains paramount for the farmers of IFAP; however, biofuels represent a new market opportunity, help diversify risk and promote rural development. Biofuels are the best option currently available to bring down greenhouse gas emissions from the transport sector and thus to help mitigate climate change. With oil prices currently at record levels, biofuels also support fuel security.

Recently, biofuels have been blamed for soaring food prices. There are many factors behind the rise in food prices, including supply shortages due to poor weather conditions, and changes in eating habits which are generating strong demand. The proportion of agricultural land given over to producing biofuels in the world is very small: 1 percent in Brazil, 1 percent in Europe, 4 percent in the United States of America, and so biofuel production is a marginal factor in the rise in food prices.

The misconceptions about biofuels are important to overcome for a farming community that has long suffered from low incomes. Bioenergy represents a good opportunity to boost rural economies and reduce poverty, provided this production complies with sustainability criteria. Sustainable biofuel production by family farmers is not a threat to food production. It is an opportunity to achieve profitability and to revive rural communities.

Development of biofuels depends on positive public policy frameworks and incentives such as mandatory targets for biofuel use and fiscal incentives that favour biofuels relative to fossil fuels until the industry matures. This is in the public interest when biofuels are produced from local sources since they create employment and wealth in the country. Governments should also provide investment incentives including: income tax credits for small biofuel producers, financing bioenergy plants, increasing farmers' participation through matching grants, and reducing business risk for the adoption of new technologies. Support for research and development, particularly for small-scale technology and enhancing the energy potential of indigenous plants, is crucial.

Biofuels are not a miracle solution, but they offer significant income opportunities for farmers. If farmers are to benefit, careful long-term assessment of economic, environmental and social benefits and costs are required to identify real opportunities aimed at improving producers' incomes. Sound strategies, developed along with the different stakeholders, are needed to capture the potential environmental and economic benefits, including the setting up of a rational land-use policy, appropriate selection of crops and production areas, and protection of rights of farmers. Farmers' organizations need to push for the creation of the right incentive mechanisms that will allow their members to benefit from this new opportunity and generate complementary incomes.

Further research and development are needed in order to avoid competition between food and fuel uses of certain crops and also to get the right signals regarding the development of biofuel production worldwide. Therefore, bridging the knowledge gap on biofuels through information dissemination and capacity building programmes to support farmers in developing ownership of the value chain are of utmost importance.

Part II

WORLD FOOD AND
AGRICULTURE IN REVIEW

Part II

World food and agriculture in review

World food and agriculture are facing critical challenges. Sharply higher food prices sparked riots in many countries in 2008 and have led at least 40 governments to impose emergency measures such as food price controls or export restrictions (FAO, 2008a). Meanwhile, food-aid volumes have fallen to their lowest levels in 40 years (WFP, 2008) even as the number of countries requiring emergency assistance has grown. While higher commodity prices offer opportunities for agricultural producers to increase production and earn higher incomes, early assessments of current crop-year conditions in many countries give cause for concern (USDA, 2008b). These were among the issues discussed in June 2008 in Rome at the High Level Conference on World Food Security: the Challenges of Climate Change and Bioenergy.

Among the factors responsible for the recent surge in commodity prices are higher costs of production driven by rising petroleum prices, weather-related production shortfalls in key exporting countries and strong demand growth – including for biofuel feedstocks. These factors occurred against a backdrop of historically low global cereal stocks, driving market prices higher. Some of the emergency measures implemented to protect consumers from higher prices, such as export controls, have further destabilized world markets (FAO, 2008a).

While commodity prices have always risen and fallen with changes in supply and demand, world agriculture now appears to be undergoing a structural shift towards a higher demand-growth path. Many countries, especially in Asia, have entered a period of faster economic growth that is generating strong demand for higher-quality diets including more meat, dairy products and vegetable oils (FAO, 2007d; Pingali, 2007). The growth in demand arising from stronger income growth is certainly welcome news, but higher prices pose challenges for all consumers, particularly the poorest.

Liquid biofuels constitute a second major new source of demand for agricultural products, as discussed in depth in Part I of this report. The degree to which biofuel demand has influenced recent food and commodity price trends is a matter of debate, with estimates ranging from 3 percent (USDA, 2008b) to 30 percent (IFPRI, 2008) and higher. Analysis reported in Part I suggests that the projected growth in biofuel demand over the next decade is likely to push commodity prices 12–15 percent above the levels that would have prevailed in 2017 if biofuels were held at 2007 levels (OECD–FAO, 2008).

Some of the supply factors that have contributed to the current high prices are transitory in nature, such as poor crop-growing conditions in a few regions. Better weather can increase production and bring prices back to more normal levels. Farmers can also respond to higher prices by increasing crop area and intensifying the use of yield-enhancing technologies. Other factors, such as growing demand as a result of rising incomes and expanding biofuel production, will continue to exert upward pressure on prices.

Decades of depressed commodity prices have led many governments in developing countries to neglect investments in agricultural productivity, and higher petroleum prices may signal a long-term shift in the cost of agricultural production, making it more costly for farmers to intensify production. Moreover, global climate change is predicted to increase the frequency and severity of extreme weather events. These longer-term factors pose serious challenges to the global food and agriculture system.

This review of the state of food and agriculture briefly summarizes the current situation with a view to illuminating the underlying causes of the current agricultural situation and anticipating future commodity-market developments. It also analyses some of the leading sources of uncertainty facing world agriculture and presents a series of scenarios outlining the possible implications of alternative assumptions regarding the key factors underpinning the recent agricultural commodity price surge. To help inform some of the key issues raised at the June 2008 High Level Conference, scenarios are presented for alternative developments in biofuel production, petroleum prices, income growth, crop yields and trade policies.

AGRICULTURAL COMMODITY PRICES

The FAO index of nominal food prices doubled between 2002 and 2008 (Figure 30). Energy prices, led by crude oil, began rising earlier, in 1999, and have trebled since 2002. In order to assess how nominal price increases affect consumers, they need to be considered in relation to prices of other goods and changes in purchasing power. Figure 30 also shows food prices deflated by an index of prices for traded manufactured goods. This real food price index began rising in 2002, after four decades of predominantly declining trends, and spiked sharply upwards in 2006 and 2007. By mid-2008, real food prices were 64 percent above the levels of 2002. The only other period of significantly rising real food prices since this data series began occurred in the early 1970s in the wake of the first international oil crisis.

Affordability is a question of income as well as prices. Figure 31 shows an index of four major commodities – vegetable oils, wheat, maize and rice – deflated by an index of per capita world gross domestic product (GDP). The figure shows that, until recently, these commodities have generally become more affordable in terms of average purchasing power throughout the period since the mid-1970s.

The lower graph in Figure 31 shows the same index but only since 2000, making the recent changes more visible. Vegetable oil prices have risen twice as fast as average incomes since 2000, and other commodity prices have also risen substantially relative to incomes: wheat by 61 percent, maize by 32 percent and rice by 29 percent. For the last three crops, most of the increase has occurred since 2005. These rapid increases have led to a substantial loss of purchasing power. The averages, of course, hide wide variations among and within countries. For countries where per capita GDP growth has lagged the world average, the loss of purchasing power would be even greater. Similarly, within countries, low-income consumers who rely on basic food commodities for the bulk of their diets would be most acutely affected.

World price changes do not necessarily translate directly into local consumer prices. The degree of price transmission depends on several factors, including currency exchange rates, trade openness, the efficiency of markets and government policies for price stabilization. To illustrate this point, Figure 32 shows the evolution of rice prices from late 2003 to late 2007 for five Asian countries. During this period, world prices denominated in US dollars increased by 56 percent, the same for all countries. Prices at the border expressed in national currency

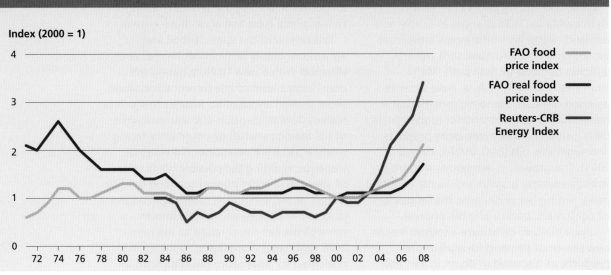

FIGURE 30
Long-term food and energy price trends, real and nominal

Index (2000 = 1)

FAO food price index
FAO real food price index
Reuters-CRB Energy Index

Source: FAO.

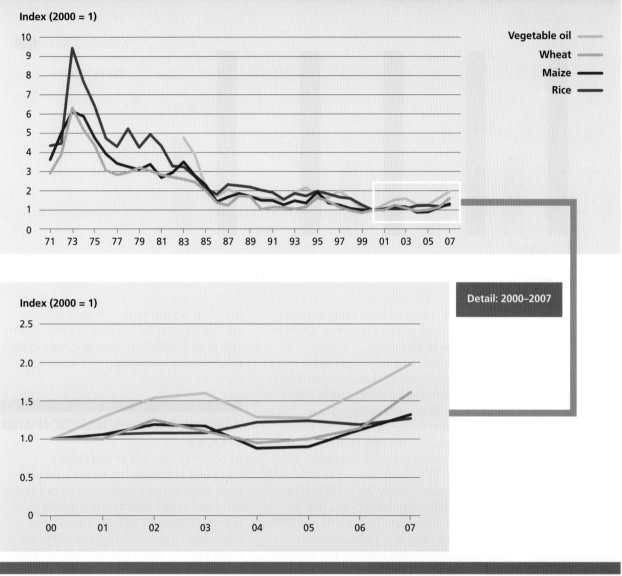

FIGURE 31
Commodity prices relative to income, 1971–2007

Source: Prices and population from OECD–FAO, 2008; GDP in current US dollars from IMF, 2008.

units also increased for all countries, but by differing amounts depending on changes in the real exchange rate between the US dollar and the national currency. The currencies of all of these countries except Bangladesh appreciated strongly against the dollar, offsetting part of the impact of higher international prices.

The domestic price changes shown in Figure 32 are based on observed prices in local markets and reflect the application of tariffs for imported goods and other market interventions aimed at buffering the effect

of international price changes. The ratio of the change in the local market price to that of the world price represents the degree of price transmission. The data show that the degree of price transmission has varied widely, from about 10 percent or less in India and the Philippines, to over 40 percent in Bangladesh, Indonesia and Thailand. During this period, several countries pursued policies aimed at insulating domestic markets from international prices. For example, India and the Philippines used government storage, procurement and distribution as

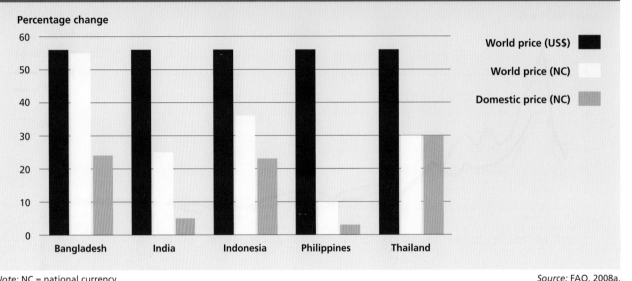

FIGURE 32
Changes in real rice prices in selected Asian countries, October–December 2003 to October–December 2007

Percentage change

Note: NC = national currency.

Source: FAO, 2008a.

well as restrictions on international trade, and Bangladesh used variable rice tariffs to stabilize domestic prices.

A low degree of price transmission should not be taken to mean that consumers have not been affected by rising prices. Prices rose by 25–30 percent in Bangladesh, India and Pakistan. Furthermore, world prices surged further in the first quarter of 2008, almost doubling between December 2007 and March 2008, and have led to substantial price increases in many domestic markets. In Bangladesh, wholesale prices rose by 38 percent during the first quarter of 2008. Prices in the India and Philippines also increased significantly during this period. Policy responses to rising prices are discussed further below and illustrated in Figure 40.

Part I of this report contains an extensive analysis of the impacts of higher food prices on food security. For the poorest households, food typically accounts for half, and often more, of their total expenditure. It follows that food price increases can have significant effects on welfare and nutrition. As shown in Figure 29 in Part I, a 10 percent increase in the price of the staple food can reduce the welfare of the poorest quintile of consumers by up to 3 percent in many countries. These estimates do not allow for household responses in production and consumption decisions. However, in the very

short run, adjustments in crop production are limited, and on the consumption side the very poor are likely to have only very limited substitution possibilities.

AGRICULTURAL PRODUCTION AND STOCKS
As noted above, one of the factors identified as driving the recent commodity price surge was weather-induced production shortfalls in key commodity-exporting regions. The index of total agricultural production from 1990 through 2006, the latest year for which comprehensive data are available, shows rising output for the world as a whole and most country groups, with the exception of developed countries, where output has been flat during most of the period (Figure 33). In per capita terms, output levelled off after 2004 for the world as a whole, and declined in the least-developed countries in 2006 after nearly a decade of modest growth.

More recent data and projections to 2010 are available from the OECD-FAO agricultural outlook for key traded crops: wheat, rice, coarse grains, rapeseed, soybean, sunflower seed, palm oil and sugar (OECD–FAO, 2008).

At the global level, total production of these commodities (converted into wheat-

FIGURE 33
Agricultural production indices, total and per capita

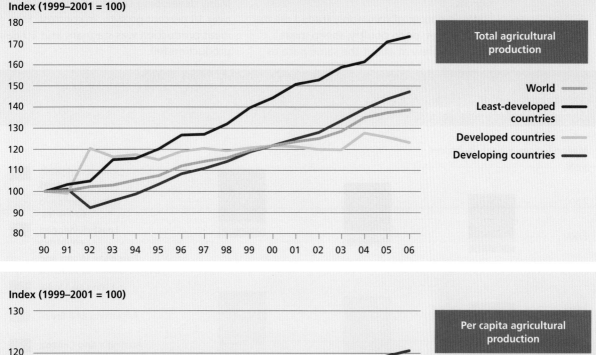

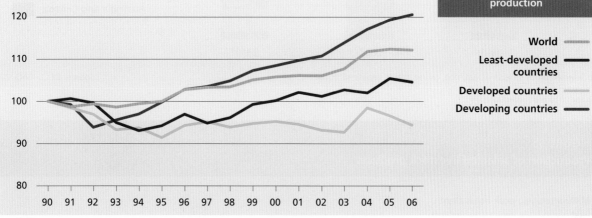

Source: FAO, 2008i.

equivalent units) rose by almost 6 percent in 2007 compared with the 2003–05 average (Figure 34).[1] However, production shortfalls of 20 percent in Australia and Canada, two major cereal exporters, contributed to tighter export supplies. Together with Argentina and Brazil, these countries account for only 15 percent of global production of these

crops but 35–40 percent of world exports. Supply disruptions in these countries can have disproportionate implications for export supplies and international agricultural prices.

Looking ahead to 2010, world output of these crops is projected to rise by 7 percent compared with 2007. This outcome depends on weather and the effective transmission of price signals to producers in countries that have the capacity to expand production. Where governments intentionally dampen price transmission, producers may not receive the necessary incentive to expand production. Conversely, where costs of

[1] Crop and livestock product volumes are converted into a common unit for comparability. Crops are aggregated on a wheat basis based on relative prices in 2000–02. Livestock products are also aggregated into a common unit based on relative prices.

fertilizers and other purchased inputs have risen rapidly along with petroleum prices, farmers may be unable to expand production despite receiving stronger price signals.

World output of commonly traded meats, namely beef, pork, poultry, sheep meat and milk, grew at about the same pace as output of traded crops from 2003–05 to 2007 (Figure 35). The 10 percent growth in developing-country output outpaced OECD production growth of 2 percent. Many developing countries posted well over 10 percent growth. In contrast, EU meat production was stagnant and EU dairy production fell.

FIGURE 34
Production of selected crops

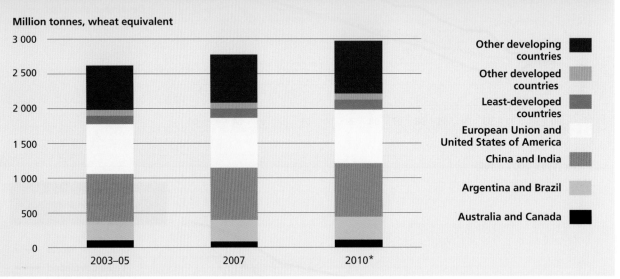

Million tonnes, wheat equivalent

Notes: Selected crops include wheat, rice, coarse grains, rapeseed, soybean, sunflower seed, palm oil and sugar.
* Data for 2010 are projections.

Source: OECD–FAO, 2008.

FIGURE 35
Production of selected livestock products

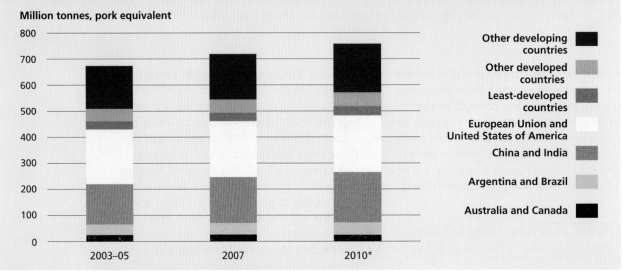

Million tonnes, pork equivalent

Note: Selected livestock products include beef, pork, poultry, sheep meat and milk.
* Data for 2010 are projections.

Source: OECD–FAO, 2008.

FIGURE 36
Ratio of global stocks to use

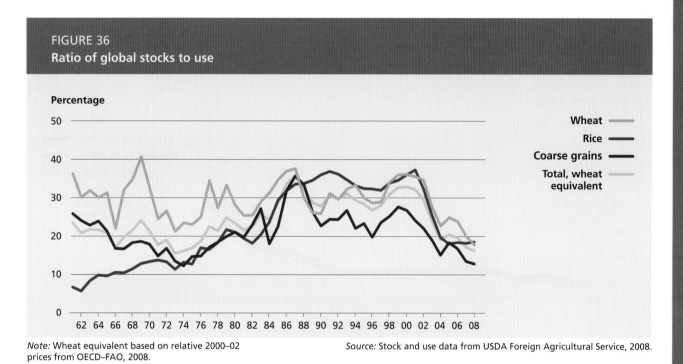

Note: Wheat equivalent based on relative 2000–02 prices from OECD–FAO, 2008.

Source: Stock and use data from USDA Foreign Agricultural Service, 2008.

During the three-year period from 2007 to 2010, these trends are generally projected to continue despite the lingering effects of higher feed costs. The rate of output expansion in some key regions is expected to slow somewhat, but to remain strong in developing countries.

Stocks have the potential to offset shocks to agricultural markets. Stocks can be drawn down quickly during periods of high prices, or built up during periods of low prices, thus offering the opportunity to smooth prices and consumption over time. Global cereal stocks (wheat, rice and coarse grains) have fallen steadily relative to use requirements since the mid-1980s and even more quickly since 2000 (Figure 36). The stocks-to-use ratio for these cereals, at 16 percent, is half the level of ten years ago. This is lower than at any time during the past 45 years. Very low stock levels can make markets more vulnerable to shocks, contributing to price volatility and overall market uncertainty.

TRADE

Global food-import expenditures, in value terms, are forecast to reach US$1 035 billion dollars in 2008, 26 percent higher than the previous peak in 2007 (Figure 37). This figure is still provisional because FAO's food import bill forecasts are conditional on developments in international prices and freight rates, which remain highly uncertain for the remainder of the year. The bulk of the anticipated growth in the world food import bill would come from higher expenditures on rice (77 percent), wheat (60 percent) and vegetable oils (60 percent). Import bills for livestock products are expected to register smaller increases, owing to moderate rises in global prices together with subdued trade. Higher international commodity prices are responsible for most of the increase, but freight costs, which have almost doubled for many routes, also contribute.

Among economic groups, the most economically vulnerable countries are set to bear the highest burden in the cost of importing food, with total expenditures by least-developed countries and low-income food-deficit countries expected to climb 37 percent and 40 percent, respectively, from 2007, after having risen almost as much in the previous year. The sustained rise in imported food expenditures for these vulnerable country groups is such that, on current expectations, by the end of 2008 their annual food import basket could cost four times as much as it did in 2000. This is in stark contrast to the trend prevailing for the overall developed country group, where import costs have risen far less.

FIGURE 37
Global food import expenditures, 1990–2008

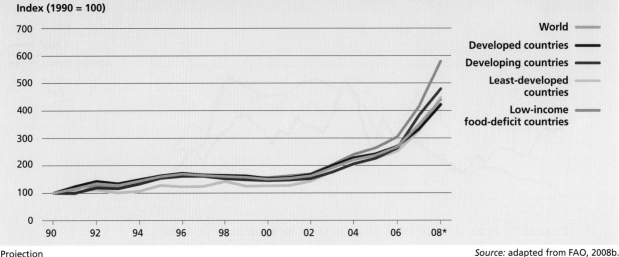

Index (1990 = 100)

World
Developed countries
Developing countries
Least-developed countries
Low-income food-deficit countries

* Projection

Source: adapted from FAO, 2008b.

FIGURE 38
Exports of selected crops

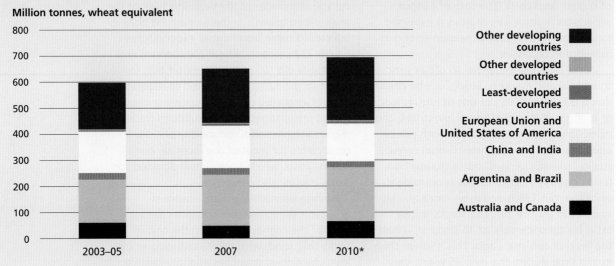

Million tonnes, wheat equivalent

Other developing countries
Other developed countries
Least-developed countries
European Union and United States of America
China and India
Argentina and Brazil
Australia and Canada

Note: Selected crops include wheat, rice, coarse grains, rapeseed, soybean, sunflower seed, palm oil and sugar.
*Data for 2010 are projections.

Source: OECD–FAO, 2008.

Imports and exports of selected commodities

The volume of major crop exports increased by 9 percent (55 billion tonnes in wheat equivalent) from 2003–05 to 2007 and is forecast to continue growing almost as rapidly to 2010 (Figure 38). Comparing trade patterns with production for major traded commodities highlights the role that imports and exports play in different countries. Supply disruptions in major exporting countries can have important implications for export supplies and international agricultural markets even if they have little impact on global production. Conversely, in cases where trade is a small share of the domestic market, minor changes in a country's supply or demand can have proportionately larger effects on trade flows.

Imports of these major crops are less concentrated than exports (Figure 39). Only China and the EU account for more than 10 percent of global imports each. Reflecting strong income growth, imports of many countries have increased in volume terms during the past three years despite higher world prices, a development that puts additional upward pressure on prices. As noted above, some countries whose currencies have appreciated relative to the US dollar have been able to sustain imports despite rising US dollar-denominated prices.

Trade and consumption policies
Many countries have adjusted their trade and consumption policies in response to higher international prices. Figure 40 reports the number of countries that have adopted policy responses to rising food prices as of May 2008. Most of the countries in the sample have changed trade or consumption policies with a view to mitigating the impact of higher prices on consumers.

Trade policies are among the most-used measures, with 18 countries reducing import tariffs on cereals and 17 imposing export restrictions. Of the latter, 14 countries have placed quantitative restrictions or outright

bans on exports. Consumption policies have included reducing food taxes (11 countries) or providing consumption subsidies (12 countries). An additional eight countries have adopted price controls. Of these measures, export bans and price controls are the most disruptive to markets and are likely to suppress incentives to producers to increase production.

FOOD AID AND FOOD EMERGENCY NEEDS
One measure of vulnerability is the number of countries requiring external food assistance. As shown in Figure 41, as of May 2008, a total of 36 countries in crisis required external assistance, either because of exceptional shortfalls in aggregate food production/supplies, widespread lack of access or severe localized food insecurity. Twenty-one of these were in Africa, ten in Asia and the Near East, four in Latin America and one in Europe.

Rising food and energy prices have implications for food aid and food emergencies. Currently, food import bills and food-aid budgets are stretched thin, as prices per unit rise and transportation costs climb. For example, between the

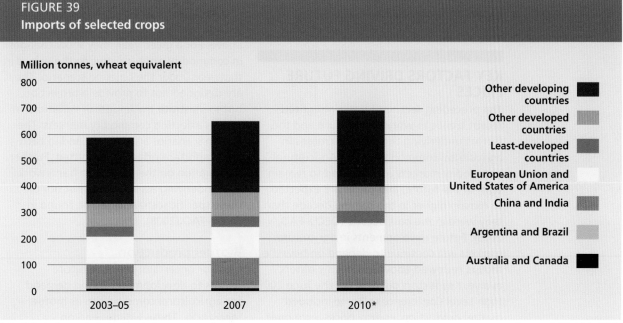

FIGURE 39
Imports of selected crops

Note: Selected crops include wheat, rice, coarse grains, rapeseed, soybean, sunflower seed, palm oil and sugar.
* Data for 2010 are projections.

Source: OECD–FAO, 2008.

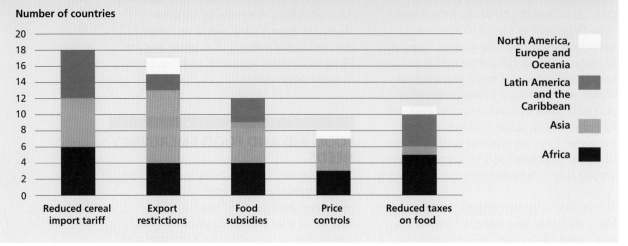

FIGURE 40
Policy responses to high food prices, by region

Number of countries

Source: FAO, 2008a.

2005/06 and 2006/07 crop years, food-aid volumes decreased by 18 percent (expressed in wheat-equivalent), while the imputed value at world prices fell by only 3 percent (Figure 42). Since 1993/94, volumes have fallen by two-thirds and the imputed value has been reduced by half, with the difference explained by higher prices. Food-aid volumes in 2007/08 reached their lowest level since the early 1970s, reflecting the inverse relationship between food-aid volumes and world prices that typifies food-aid shipments (FAO, 2006c).

KEY FACTORS DRIVING FUTURE PRICES

The preceding sections have highlighted recent trends in world agriculture and the factors underlying the sharp increases in agricultural commodity prices. Agricultural commodity markets are expected to remain tight in the future, and prices are expected to remain higher in the coming decade than they were in the past decade (OECD–FAO, 2008). Future developments in agricultural markets will continue to depend on how the factors reviewed above, and many others, evolve. Key factors discussed at the June 2008 High Level Conference in Rome included biofuel production, energy prices, economic growth, crop yields and trade policies. Some of these factors can be influenced by policy-

makers while others cannot, but none can be predicted with certainty, so a quantitative assessment of the potential impact of a range of possible values may help to gauge the range of market outcomes.

For this purpose, a series of scenarios have been assessed using the AgLink-Cosimo model, developed in a collaborative effort between the secretariats of FAO and OECD. The simulation exercises illustrate the estimated impact in the medium term on world prices of major agricultural commodities, relative to a baseline scenario, of hypothetic variations in the factors listed above. For a given year, they show changes in commodity prices relative to the values in that year under the baseline scenario. They are designed not to provide a projection, but to illustrate the impact of variations in factors affecting commodity markets. The chosen scenarios are stylized, and in each case important effects are omitted. Further information on the modelling framework and underlying assumptions (but not on these specific scenarios) can be found in OECD–FAO (2008).

Biofuel production
A major uncertainty for the future relates to developments in the demand for agricultural commodities as biofuel feedstocks. These will depend on developments in policies supporting biofuel production and consumption, on trends in

FIGURE 41
Countries in crisis requiring external assistance, May 2008

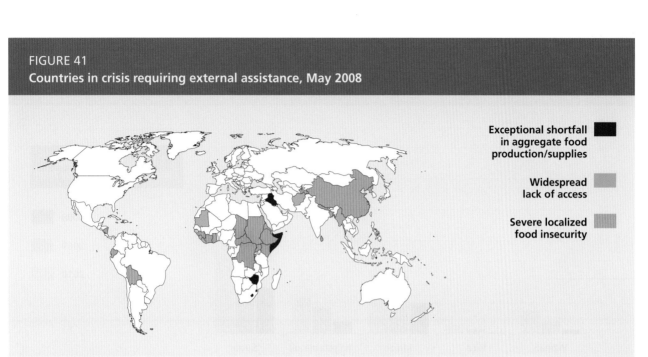

Source: FAO.

FIGURE 42
Cereal food aid, 1993/94–2006/07

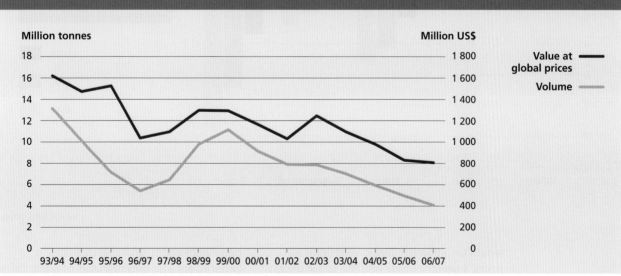

Note: The volume of cereal food aid is the simple sum, not in wheat equivalent. Value is based on the quantity of each cereal multiplied by the global price.

Source: FAO, based on data from WFP, 2008.

petroleum prices and on developments in technologies and their application. Relative to a baseline scenario where biofuel feedstock demand remains at the level of 2007, two different alternative scenarios have been analysed:

- an increase in biofuel demand for coarse grains, sugar and vegetable oil of 30 percent by 2010 (that is, implying a trend towards a doubling in ten years);

- a decline in biofuel demand for these commodities by 15 percent by 2010 (implying a trend towards a halving in ten years).

The effects on world prices of wheat, rice, maize, vegetable oil and sugar, relative to the baseline of biofuel feedstocks remaining at 2007 levels, are illustrated in Figure 43. In the case of a 15 percent reduction in biofuel feedstock use by 2010, world maize prices

FIGURE 43

Effects on global agricultural prices of rising or falling biofuel feedstock use
(compared with constant use at 2007 levels)

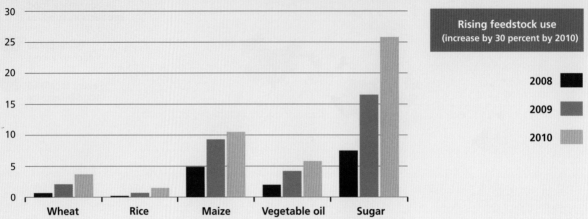

Percentage change

Rising feedstock use
(increase by 30 percent by 2010)

2008
2009
2010

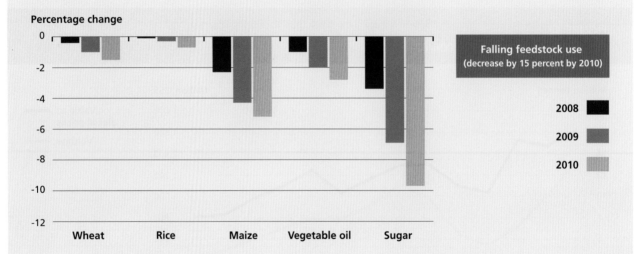

Percentage change

Falling feedstock use
(decrease by 15 percent by 2010)

2008
2009
2010

Source: FAO, 2008c.

would be 5 percent lower, vegetable oil prices 3 percent lower and the sugar prices 10 percent lower than the baseline scenario. In contrast, an increase of 30 percent in biofuel feedstock use by 2010 would cause prices in that year to increase by as much as 26 percent in the case of sugar and by 11 and 6 percent, respectively, for maize and vegetable oil. In both cases, there would be smaller effects in the same direction for wheat and rice.

Petroleum prices

Petroleum prices are one factor affecting demand for biofuel feedstocks. However,

petroleum prices, and energy prices in general, are also determinants of agricultural production costs through their effects on the prices of fuel and agricultural chemicals. Stages between production and consumption of agricultural commodities, such as transportation and processing, are also sensitive to energy prices, but are not considered here.

The impact of petroleum prices on agricultural commodity markets is assessed by estimating the effect of higher or lower petroleum prices relative to a baseline scenario where petroleum prices remain at US$130 per barrel, the assumed

FIGURE 44

Effects on global agricultural prices of rising or falling petroleum prices
(compared with constant price at US$130/barrel)

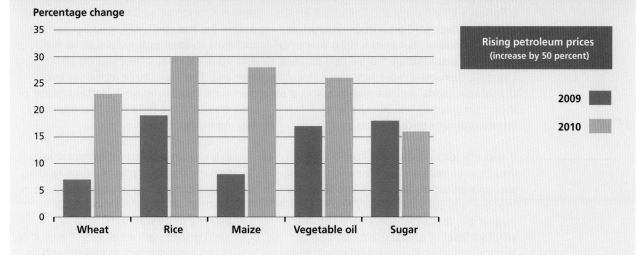

Percentage change

Rising petroleum prices
(increase by 50 percent)

2009
2010

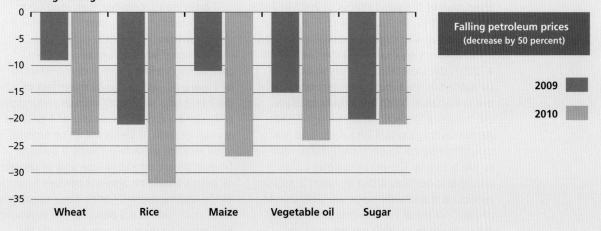

Percentage change

Falling petroleum prices
(decrease by 50 percent)

2009
2010

Source: FAO, 2008c.

average level for 2008. Two cases are considered:

- petroleum prices rising to US$195 per barrel in 2009 and 2010 (50 percent above the base level of US$130);
- petroleum prices falling to US$65 per barrel in 2009 and 2010 (50 percent below the base level).

The effects on the costs of production and on biofuel feedstock demand are both considered.

The results of the simulation on prices of key agricultural commodities are shown in Figure 44. A halving of oil prices would lead to a significant decline in agricultural commodity prices, ranging from 21 to 32 percent in 2010, depending on the commodity. Conversely, a doubling of petroleum prices would lead to higher commodity prices in the range of 16–30 percent.

Income growth

Strong demand growth from rising incomes and purchasing power in several parts of the developing world has been a major factor explaining part of the recent price increases. Such developments and the overall macroeconomic environment are sources of considerable uncertainty for agricultural markets.

Figure 45 illustrates the impact on crop prices of a halving of GDP growth in 2008, 2009 and 2010 compared with a situation of continued growth at the rates experienced in each country in 2007. Exchange rates and inflation are held constant. The initial effects of much slower GDP growth on crop prices would be modest, but by the third year price reductions would range from 6 to 9 percent. Livestock demand is more sensitive to income than staple foods, and livestock markets (not shown on graphic) would experience much more significant price impacts.

Yield shocks and yield trends

Weather-related shocks yields and to supply explain part of the recent commodity price increase, and such shocks may become more frequent in the future. Given the current very low level of global grain stocks, the implications of additional yield shocks may be more pronounced.

Figure 46 illustrates the impact of a repetition of the yield shocks of 2007 in 2008, 2009 and 2010. If global wheat, rice, maize, vegetable oil and sugar yields were reduced by an amount equivalent to the yield shock of 2007, the expected recovery in output contained in the baseline projections would not materialize. With few stocks to draw on, the price impacts would be significant. Annual average prices for wheat and maize would rise by 20–25 percent in 2008, relative to the baseline. Other commodity prices would also be higher, but by lesser amounts, reflecting the smaller negative yield shocks of 2007 for these commodities. Repeating the yield shock in 2009 would produce further price increases relative to the baseline, reflecting increasingly tight stock levels. A further yield shock in 2010 would again raise prices relative to the baseline, but by lesser amounts than in 2008 and 2009 for wheat and maize, because of the potential for producers to expand area planted in response to higher prices, offsetting some of the decline in yields.

Repeated negative yield shocks are unlikely to occur on a global scale, and such a scenario lends itself to inappropriately pessimistic conclusions. Positive yield shocks in the form of bumper crops are also possible. A good year for growing crops in most key producing areas could lead to a partial respite from the tight market situation, leaving room even to begin rebuilding stocks. In such a situation, prices could fall quickly.

Apart from transitory yield shocks, trends in yield growth are relevant to the long-term evolution of agricultural markets and determine the ability of world agriculture to adjust to structural shifts such as the emergence of major new sources of demand. The magnitude of yield growth over time constitutes an important factor of uncertainty in the long run. Two opposing arguments can be made.

- Yield growth will be constrained, even negative in some regions due to climatic changes, possibly even leading to declining global yields. Moreover, weather-related yield shocks will become more common.
- Yield growth will accelerate if high crop prices are sustained, as investments in new technologies increase and more producers see profits from raising their own yields, possibly even leading to substantial yield growth in developing countries.

The impact of different assumptions concerning yield growth is demonstrated by Figure 47, which shows the effect of a doubling or a halving of annual yield growth relative to a baseline scenario of 1 percent annual growth. If yields for all commodities in all regions were to grow by 2 percent from 2008 on, wheat, maize and vegetable oil prices would be about 2 percent lower in 2010. Alternatively, if yields were to grow at an annual rate of 0.5 percent, prices would be higher, again most pronouncedly for wheat, maize and vegetable oil. In the longer run the impact of different yield growth assumptions can be significant. Thus, in the case of maize, after ten years of greater yield growth the global price would be 5 percent lower; and after ten years of lower yield growth the price would be 2.5 percent higher.

Trade policy responses

Policy-makers are under pressure to respond to popular concerns over rising food prices. Responses have included trade measures aimed at influencing domestic prices. In several cases, as noted earlier, importing countries have lowered tariffs and exporting countries have taxed or restricted exports.

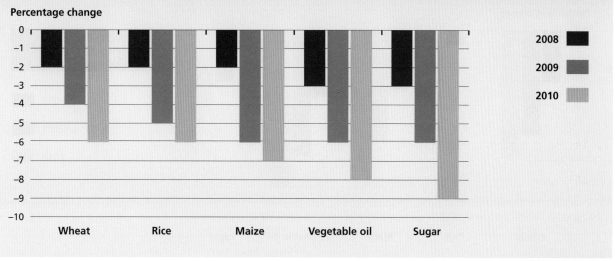

FIGURE 45

Effects on global agricultural prices of a halving of GDP growth
(compared with GDP growth rate at 2007 levels)

Source: FAO, 2008c.

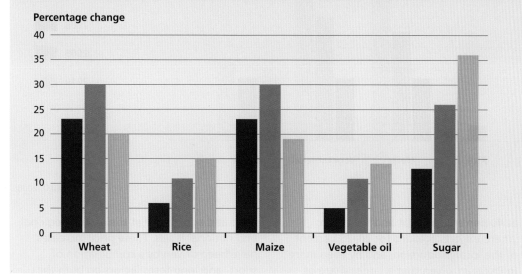

FIGURE 46

Effects on global agricultural prices of a repetition of the 2007 yield shocks

Source: FAO, 2008c.

In either case, the implications are lower domestic prices but further upward pressure on global prices. The lower domestic prices will reduce domestic producers' incentives to increase output and will consequently tend to impede their supply response, thus protracting the situation of high prices.

The impacts of export restrictions are illustrated by a hypothetical scenario considering Egypt, India, Pakistan and Viet Nam, which together accounted for 38 percent of global rice exports in 2007. If these countries were to engage in policies that halved their rice exports in 2008, the global price would rise by an estimated 20 percent in that year. Relative to a situation with no export barriers, domestic rice prices would fall by as much

FIGURE 47

Effects on global agricultural prices of higher and lower annual yield growth
(compared with yield growth rate of 1 percent)

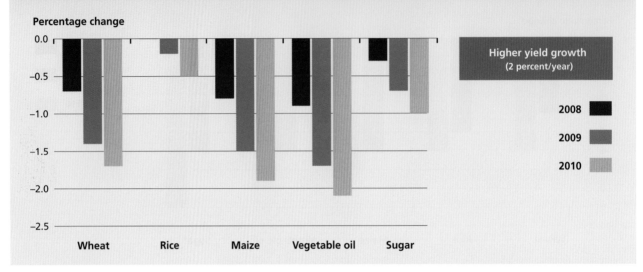

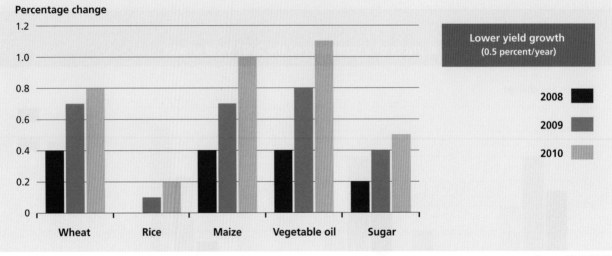

Source: FAO, 2008c.

as 40 percent in Egypt and Viet Nam, where exports account for 20–25 percent of the local production, and by even more in Pakistan, given that a larger share of Pakistan's production is exported. The lower domestic prices in 2008 would depress production significantly in 2009.

LOOKING AHEAD

Agricultural prices have always been volatile, but recent sharp increases in global agricultural commodity prices have focused unprecedented attention on the state of

food and agriculture at the global, regional and national levels. These price increases have been driven by a combination of short- and long-term factors on both the supply and demand sides, some of which will persist into the future. Looking ahead, we expect that biofuels will remain a significant source of increased demand for agricultural commodities – and for the resources used to produce them – and that the growth in income and consumption levels in developing countries will continue and, it is hoped, spread. On the supply side, the incidence of both short-term yield shocks and longer-term climate change remain uncertain, indicating the persistence of price volatility given low levels of stocks.

Regardless of the source or magnitude of factors raising price levels and volatility, four essential steps are supported by the international community, and have been articulated most recently in the declaration of the High Level Conference on World Food Security: the Challenges of Climate Change and Bioenergy, as adopted in Rome in June 2008.

First, the immediate crisis must be addressed by providing appropriate safety nets for the most vulnerable countries and people. The decline in food-aid shipments in 2007/08, as food prices soared, is an urgent reminder that food aid can be an essential component of emergency aid, but it cannot form the basis of a durable food security strategy. More food aid is urgently required, but it is not enough. Other safety nets could include direct income support or food vouchers for low-income consumers who have seen their purchasing power eroded by rising prices. Many countries have put in place price controls in an effort to insulate consumers from world prices, but such measures are costly and inefficient because they benefit many who are not needy. Furthermore, such measures can be counterproductive in the longer run because they undermine the incentives for farmers to increase production and they reduce the resilience of the food system.

Second, there is an urgent need to invest in agriculture to enable the sector to take advantage of the opportunities presented by higher prices. Global agricultural output must increase substantially in the coming years to meet the rapidly growing demand arising from faster income growth and biofuel production. This growth must be sustainable and take into consideration the already fragile condition of many agricultural ecosystems. Such interventions should be designed in such a way as to encourage the emergence of market-based input supply systems, again to strengthen the resilience of the food system. To reduce the risks associated with high prices and to share the opportunities more widely, particular attention must be paid to the needs of small farmers in developing countries, and to the encouragement of sustainable production practices.

Third, as agreed at the High Level Conference, it is essential to address the challenges and opportunities posed by biofuels, in view of the world's food-security, energy and sustainable development needs. In-depth studies, an exchange of experiences on biofuel technologies, norms and regulations, and a coherent, effective and results-oriented international dialogue on biofuels are necessary to ensure that production and use of biofuels are economically, environmentally and socially sustainable, and that they take into account the need to achieve and maintain global food security.

Finally, the international community needs to act urgently to strengthen the credibility and resilience of the international trade system. International trade can be an important source of market stabilization, allowing countries to meet local production shortfalls through the market. But short-term measures, such as export bans aimed at protecting domestic consumers, can further destabilize markets and punish countries that depend on imports for their food security. More stable and transparent trade rules can support the resilience of food systems and promote durable food security. Only with these measures in place can we look forward to an agriculture sector that is more productive, more resilient and better placed to meet the challenges of continuing uncertainty and increasing demand.

- **References**

- **Special chapters of**
  The State of Food and Agriculture

References

Ahluwalia, M.S. 1978. Rural poverty and agricultural performance in India. *Journal of Development Studies,* 14(3): 298–323.

Anderson, K. & Valenzuela, E. 2007. The World Trade Organization's Doha Cotton Initiative: a tale of two issues. *The World Economy,* 30(8): 1281–1304.

Anríquez, G. & López, R. 2007. Agricultural growth and poverty in an archetypical middle income country: Chile 1987–2003. *Agricultural Economics,* 36: 191–202.

Azar, C. & Larson, E.D. 2000. Bioenergy and land-use competition in Northeast Brazil. *Energy for Sustainable Development,* IV(3): 64–71.

Banse, M., van Meijl, H., Tabeau, A. & Woltjer, G. 2008. *The impact of biofuel policies on global agricultural production, trade and land use.* Background paper for the FAO Expert Meeting on Bioenergy Policy, Markets and Trade and Food Security, 18–20 February 2008. Rome, FAO.

Barrett, C. 2008. Smallholder market participation: concepts and evidence from eastern and southern Africa. *Food Policy,* 33(4): 299–317.

Beck, T. & Nesmith, C. 2000. Building on poor people's capacities: the case of common property resources in India and West Africa. *World Development,* 29(1): 119–133.

Binswanger, H.P. & von Braun, J. 1991. Technological change and commercialization in agriculture: the effect on the poor. *The World Bank Research Observer,* 6(1): 57–80.

Birur, D.K., Hertel, T.W. & Tyner, W.E. 2007. *The biofuels boom: implications for world food markets.* Paper prepared for the OECD/Netherlands Food Economy Conference 2007, 18–19 October 2007. The Hague.

Block, S., Kiess, L., Webb, P., Kosen, S., Moench-Pfanner, R., Bloem, M.W. & Timmer, C.P. 2004. Macro shocks and micro outcomes: child nutrition during Indonesia's crisis. *Economics and Human Biology,* 2(1): 21–44.

Boughton, D. & de Frahan, B.H. 1994. *Agricultural research impact assessment: the case of maize technology adoption in Southern Mali.* International Development Working Paper No. 41. East Lansing, MI, USA, Michigan State University.

Bouis, H. & Haddad, L.J. 1994. The nutrition effects of sugarcane cropping in a southern Philippine province. In J. von Braun & E. Kennedy, eds. *Agricultural commercialization, economic development, and nutrition.* Baltimore, MD, USA, The Johns Hopkins University Press.

Bravo-Ortega, C. & Lederman, D. 2005. *Agriculture and national welfare around the world: causality and heterogeneity since 1960.* World Bank Policy Research Working Paper No. 3499. Washington, DC, World Bank.

Buarque de Hollanda, J. & Poole, A.D. 2001. *Sugar cane as an energy source in Brazil.* Rio de Janeiro, Brazil, Instituto Nacional de Eficiência Energética.

Cassman, K.G., Wood, S., Choo, P.S., Cooper, H.D., Devendra, C., Dixon, J., Gaskell, J., Kahn, S., Lal, R., Lipper, L., Pretty, J., Primavera, J., Ramankutty, N., Viglizzo, E. & Wiebe, K. 2005. Cultivated systems. In *Ecosystems and human well-being: current state and trends,* pp. 745–794. Millennium Ecosystem Assessment Series Vol. 1, edited by R. Hassan, R. Scholes & N. Ash. Washington, DC, Island Press.

CBD (Convention on Biological Diversity). 2008. *The potential impact of biofuels on biodiversity.* Note by the Executive Secretary for the Conference of the Parties to the Convention on Biological Diversity, 19–30 May 2008, Bonn, Germany (draft, 7 February 2008).

CFC (Common Fund for Commodities). 2007. *Biofuels: strategic choices for commodity dependent countries.* Commodities Issues Series. Amsterdam.

Comprehensive Assessment of Water Management in Agriculture. 2007. *Water for food, water for life: a comprehensive assessment of water management in agriculture.* London, Earthscan and Colombo, International Water Management Institute.

Coulter, J., Goodland, A., Tallontire, A. & Stringfellow, R. 1999. *Marrying farmer cooperation and contract farming for service provision in a liberalising sub-Saharan Africa.* Natural Resources Perspective No. 48. London, Overseas Development Institute.

Council of the European Union. 2007. Presidency Conclusions of the European Council (8/9 March 2007). Doc 7224/1/07 REV 1. Brussels.

Curran, L.M., Trigg, S.N., McDonald, A.K., Astiani, D., Hardiono, Y.M., Siregar, P., Caniago, I. & Kasischke, C. 2004. Lowland forest loss in protected areas of Indonesian Borneo. *Science,* 303(5660): 1000–1003.

Datt, G. & Ravallion, M. 1998. Why have some Indian states done better than others at reducing rural poverty? *Economica,* 65(257): 17–38.

de Fraiture, C., Giordano, M. & Yongsong, L. 2007. *Biofuels and implications for agricultural water use: blue impacts of green energy.* Paper presented at the International Conference on Linkages between Energy and Water Management for Agriculture in Developing Countries, ICRISAT Campus, Hyderabad, India, 29–30 January 2007. Colombo, International Water Management Institute.

Dey, J. 1981. Gambian women: unequal partners in rice development projects? *Journal of Development Studies,* 19(3): 109–122.

Dioné, J. 1989. *Informing food security policy in Mali: interactions between technology, institutions and market reforms.* East Lansing, MI, USA, Michigan State University. Ph.D. dissertation.

Doornbosch, R. & Steenblik, R. 2007. *Biofuels: is the cure worse than the disease?* Document No. SG/SD/RT(2007)3 prepared for the Round Table on Sustainable Development, 11–12 September 2007. Paris, Organisation for Economic Co-operation and Development.

Dufey, A. 2006. *Biofuels production, trade and sustainable development: emerging issues.* Sustainable Markets Discussion Paper No. 2. London, International Institute for Environment and Development.

Enkvist, P.-A., Naucler, T. & Rosander, J. 2007. A cost curve for greenhouse gas reductions. *The McKinsey Quarterly,* February.

Euler, H. & Gorriz, D. 2004. *Case study on* Jatropha curcas. Study commissioned by the Global Facilitation Unit for Underutilized Species (GFU) and the Deutsche Gesellschaft für Technische Zusammenarbeit (GTZ).

Evenson, R.E. & Gollin, D. 2003. Assessing the impact of the green revolution 1960–2000. *Science,* 300(5620): 758–762.

Faaij, A. 2007. *Framing biomass potentials: what are sustainable potentials for bioenergy?* Paper presented at the First FAO Technical Consultation on Bioenergy and Food Security, 16–18 April 2007, Rome.

Fan, S. 2002. *Agricultural research and urban poverty in India.* Environment and Production Technology Division Discussion Paper No. 94. Washington, DC, International Food Policy Research Institute.

Fan, S., Zhang, L. & Zhang, X. 2000. *Growth and poverty in rural China: the role of public investments.* Environment and Production Technology Division Discussion Paper No. 66. Washington, DC, International Food Policy Research Institute.

Fan, S., Zhang, X. & Rao, N. 2004. *Public expenditure, growth, and poverty reduction in rural Uganda.* Development Strategy and Governance Division Discussion Paper No. 4. Washington, DC, International Food Policy Research Institute.

FAO. 2001. *Contract farming, partnerships for growth: a guide,* by C. Eaton & A.W. Shepherd. FAO Agricultural Services Bulletin No. 145. Rome.

FAO. 2003. *World agriculture: towards 2015/2030. An FAO perspective,* edited by J. Bruinsma. Rome, FAO and London, Earthscan.

FAO. 2004a. *UBET – Unified Bioenergy Terminology.* Rome.

FAO. 2004b. *Price transmission in selected agricultural markets,* by P. Conforti. Commodity and Trade Policy Research Working Paper No. 7. Rome.

FAO. 2004c. *The State of Food and Agriculture 2003–04: agricultural biotechnology: meeting the needs of the poor?* FAO Agriculture Series No. 35. Rome.

FAO. 2004d. *Socio-economic analysis and policy implications of the roles of agriculture in developing countries.* Research Programme Summary Report 2004. Roles of Agriculture Project. Rome.

FAO. 2005. *The State of Food and Agriculture 2005: agricultural trade and poverty: can trade work for the poor?* FAO Agriculture Series No. 36. Rome.

FAO. 2006a. *Impact of an increased biomass use on agricultural markets, prices and food security: a longer-term perspective,* by J. Schmidhuber. Rome (available at www.fao.org/es/ESD/pastgstudies.html).

FAO. 2006b. *The State of Food Insecurity in the World 2006.* Rome.

FAO. 2006c. *The State of Food and Agriculture 2006: food aid for food security?* FAO Agriculture Series No. 37. Rome.

FAO. 2007a. The Role of Agricultural Biotechnologies for Production of Bioenergy in Developing Countries. Seminar, 12 October 2007, Rome, Italy. Organized by the FAO Working Group on Biotechnology and the FAO Working Group on Bioenergy. Rome (seminar papers available at www.fao.org/biotech/seminaroct2007.htm).

FAO. 2007b. *Recent trends in the law and policy of bioenergy production, promotion and use.* FAO Legislative Study No. 95. Rome.

FAO. 2007c. *Rural development and poverty reduction: is agriculture still the key?* by G. Anríquez & K. Stamoulis. ESA Working Paper No. 07-02. Rome

FAO. 2007d. *The State of Food and Agriculture 2007: paying farmers for environmental services.* FAO Agriculture Series No. 38. Rome.

FAO. 2008a. *Soaring food prices: facts, perspectives, impacts and actions required.* Document HLC/08/INF/1 prepared for the High-Level Conference on World Food Security: The Challenges of Climate Change and Bioenergy, 3–5 June 2008, Rome.

FAO. 2008b. *Food Outlook.* June 2008. Rome.

FAO. 2008c. *Ongoing biofuel policy scenario analysis based on the joint OECD-FAO AgLink-Cosimo model,* by M. Cluff, E. Amrouk, and M. von Lampe. Unpublished. Rome.

FAO. 2008d. *Biofuels: back to the future?* by U.R. Fritsche, SOFA 2008 background paper. Unpublished. Rome.

FAO. 2008e. *Grain production and export potential in CIS countries.* Paper prepared for the European Bank for Reconstruction and Development/FAO Conference: Fighting Food Inflation Through Sustainable Investment, 10 March 2008, London.

FAO. 2008f. *Have recent increases in international cereal prices been transmitted to domestic economies? The experience in seven large Asian countries,* by D. Dawe. ESA Working Paper 08-03. Rome.

FAO. 2008g. *How good enough biofuel governance can help rural livelihoods: making sure that biofuel development works for small farmers and communities,* by O. Dubois. SOFA 2008 background paper. Unpublished. Rome.

FAO. 2008h. *Gender and equity issues in liquid biofuels production: minimizing the risks to maximize the opportunities,* by A. Rossi and Y. Lambrou. Rome.

FAO. 2008i. *FAOSTAT statistical database.* Rome (available at http://faostat.fao.org).

FAO. Forthcoming (a). *A framework for bioenergy environmental impact analysis.* Rome.

FAO. Forthcoming (b). *Modelling the bioenergy and food security nexus: an analytical framework,* by D. Dawe, E. Felix, I. Maltsoglou & M. Salvatore. Environment and Natural Resource Management Working Paper Series. Rome.

FAO. Forthcoming (c). *The State of Agricultural Commodity Markets 2008.* Rome.

FAO. Forthcoming (d). *The State of Food Insecurity in the World 2008.* Rome.

Fargione, J., Hill, J., Tilman,D., Polasky, S. & Hawthorne, P. 2008. Land clearing and the biofuel carbon debt. *Sciencexpress,* 7 February.

Fischer, G. 2008. *Implications for land use change.* Paper presented at the Expert Meeting on Global Perspectives on Fuel and Food Security, 18–20 February 2008. Rome, FAO.

F.O. Licht (Licht Interactive Data). 2007. Database of world commodity statistics (available by subscription at www.agra-net.com/portal/home.jsp?pagetitle=showad&pubId=ag083).

Francis, G., Edinger, R. & Becker, K. 2005. A concept for simultaneous wasteland reclamation, fuel production, and socio-economic development in degraded areas in India: need, potential and perspectives of jatropha plantations. *Natural Resources Forum,* 29: 12–24.

Fresco, L.O. (with D. Dijk and W. de Ridder). 2007. *Biomass, food & sustainability: is there a dilemma?* Utrecht, Netherlands, Rabobank.

GBEP (Global Bioenergy Partnership). 2007. *A review of the current state of bioenergy development in G8+5 countries.* Rome, GBEP Secretariat, FAO.

Gonsalves, J.B. 2006. *An assessment of the biofuels industry in India.* UNCTAD/DITC/TED/2006/6. Geneva, Switzerland, United Nations Conference on Trade and Development.

Govereh, J. & Jayne, T.S. 2003. Cash cropping and food productivity: synergies or trade-offs? *Agricultural Economics,* 28: 39–50.

Hayami, Y. 2002. Family farms and plantations in tropical development. *Asian Development Review,* 19(2): 67–89.

Hayami,Y., Quisumbing, M.A. & Adriano L.S. 1990. *Toward an alternative land reform paradigm: a Philippine perspective.* Quezon City, Philippines, Ateneo de Manila University Press.

Hazell, P. & Haggblade, S. 1993. Farm-nonfarm growth linkages and the welfare of the poor. *In* M. Lipton & J. van der Gaad, eds. *Including the poor.* Proceedings of a symposium organized by the World Bank and the International Food Policy Research Institute. World Bank Regional and Sectoral Study. Washington, DC, World Bank.

Hazell, P. & Wood, S. 2008. Drivers of change in global agriculture. *Philosophical Transactions of the Royal Society B,* 363(1491): 495–515.

Heller, J. 1996. *Physic nut.* Jatropha curcas L. *Promoting the conservation and use of underutilized and neglected crops. 1.* Gatersleben, Germany, Institute of Plant

Genetics and Crop Plant Research/Rome, International Plant Genetic Resources Institute.

Hill, J., Nelson, E., Tilman, D., Polasky, S. & Tiffany, D. 2006. Environmental, economic, and energetic costs and benefits of biodiesel and ethanol biofuels. *Proceedings of the National Academy of Sciences,* 103(30): 11206–11210.

IEA (International Energy Agency). 2004. *Biofuels for transport: an international perspective.* Paris, OECD/IEA.

IEA. 2006. *World Energy Outlook 2006.* Paris.

IEA. 2007. *World Energy Outlook 2007.* Paris.

IFAD/FAO/UNF. 2008. International consultation on pro-poor Jatropha development (consultation papers available at www.ifad.org/events/jatropha).

IFPRI (International Food Policy Research Institute). 2008. *Biofuels and grain prices: impacts and policy responses.* Mark W. Rosegrant. Testimony for the US Senate Committee on Homeland Security and Governmental Affairs. 7 May 2008. Washington, DC.

IMF (International Monetary Fund). 2008. *World Economic Outlook,* April.

Johnston, B.F. & Mellor, J. 1961.The role of agriculture in economic development. *American Economic Review,* 51(4): 566–593.

Jongschaap, R.E.E., Corré, W.J., Bindraban, P.S. & Brandenburg, W.A. 2007. *Claims and facts on* Jatropha curcas L*.: global* Jatropha curcas *evaluation, breeding and propagation programme.* Report 158. Wageningen, Netherlands, Plant Research International.

Kapur, J.C. 2004. Available energy resources and environmental imperatives. *World Affairs,* Issue No. V10 N1.

Kébé, D., Diakite, L. & Diawara, H. 1998. *Impact de la dévaluation du FCFA sur la productivité, la rentabilité et les performances de la filière coton (cas du Mali).* Bamako, PRISAS/INSAH-ECOFIL/IER.

Kim, S. & Dale, B. 2004. Global potential bioethanol production from wasted crops and crop residues. *Biomass Bioenergy,* 26940: 361–375.

Kojima, M. & Johnson, T. 2005. *Potential for biofuels for transport in developing countries.* Joint UNDP/World Bank Energy Sector Management Assistance Programme. Washington, DC, International Bank for Reconstruction and Development/World Bank.

Koplow, D. 2007. *Biofuels – at what cost? Government support for ethanol and biodiesel in the United States: 2007 update.* Geneva, Switzerland, Global Subsidies Initiative,

International Institute for Sustainable Development.

Larson, D. & Borrell, B. 2001. Sugar policy and reform. *In* T. Akiyama, J. Baffes, D. Larson & P. Varangis, eds. *Commodity market reforms: lessons of two decades.* Washington, DC, World Bank.

López, R. 2007. Agricultural growth and poverty reduction. *In* F. Bresciani & A. Valdés, eds. *Beyond food production: the role of agriculture in poverty reduction.* Cheltenham, UK, Edward Elgar Publishing.

Maxwell, S. & Fernando, A. 1989. Cash crops in developing countries: the issues, the facts, the policies. *World Development,* 17(11): 1677–1708.

Moreira, J.R. 2006. Bioenergy and agriculture, promises and challenges: Brazil's experience with bioenergy. *Vision 2020,* Focus 14, Brief 8 of 12. Washington, DC, International Food Policy Research Institute.

Moreira, J.R. 2007. *Water use and impacts due ethanol production in Brazil.* Paper presented at the International Conference on Linkages between Energy and Water Management for Agriculture in Developing Countries, ICRISAT Campus, Hyderabad, India, 29–30 January 2007. São Paulo, Brazil, National Reference Center on Biomass, Institute of Electrotechnology and Energy, University of São Paulo.

Msangi, S. 2008. *Biofuels, food prices and food security.* Presentation at the Expert Meeting on Global Fuel and Food Security, FAO, Rome, 18–20 February 2008 (available at www.fao.org/fileadmin/user_upload/foodclimate/presentations/EM56/Msangi.pdf).

Naylor, R., Liska, A.J., Burke, M.B., Falcon, W.P., Gaskell, J.C., Rozelle, S.D. & Cassman, K.G. 2007. The ripple effect: biofuels, food security, and the environment. *Environment,* 49(9): 31–43.

Nelson, G.C. & Robertson, R.D. 2008. *Green gold or green wash: environmental consequences of biofuels in the developing world.* Paper presented at the Allied Social Sciences Association Meeting, New Orleans, USA, 4 January 2008.

OECD–FAO (Organisation for Economic Co-operation and Development–Food and Agriculture Organization of the United Nations). 2007. *OECD–FAO Agricultural Outlook 2007–2016.* Paris.

OECD–FAO. 2008. *OECD–FAO Agricultural Outlook 2008–2017.* Paris.

Pingali, P. 2007. Westernization of Asian diets and the transformation of food systems:

implications for research and policy. *Food Policy*, 32(3): 281–298.

Quirke, D., Steenblik, R. & Warner, B. 2008. *Biofuels – at what cost? Government support for ethanol and biodiesel in Australia*. Geneva, Switzerland, Global Subsidies Initiative, International Institute for Sustainable Development.

Rajagopal, D. & Zilberman, D. 2007. *Review of environmental, economic and policy aspects of biofuels*. World Bank Policy Research Working Paper No. 4341. Washington, DC, World Bank.

Rajagopal, D., Sexton, S.E., Roland-Host, D. & Zilberman, D. 2007. Challenge of biofuel: filling the tank without emptying the stomach? *Environmental Research Letters*, 2, 30 November.

Rashid, S. 2002. *Dynamics of agricultural wage and rice price in Bangladesh: a re-examination*. Markets and Structural Studies Division Discussion Paper No. 44. Washington, DC, International Food Policy Research Institute.

Ravallion, M. 1990. Rural welfare effects of food price changes under induced wage responses: theory and evidence for Bangladesh. *Oxford Economic Papers*, 42(3): 574–585.

Ravallion, M. & Datt, G. 1996. How important to India's poor is the sector composition of economic growth. *World Bank Economic Review*, 10(1): 1–25.

Raymond, G. & Fok, M. 1994. Relations entre coton et vivrier en Afrique de l'Ouest et du Centre. Le coton affame les populations? Une fausse affirmation. *Economies et Sociétés – ISMEA. Série Développement Agroalimentaire*, 29(3–4): 221–234.

RFA (Renewable Fuels Association). 2008. Renewable Fuels Standard. Web site (available at www.ethanolrfa.org/resource/standard/)

Righelato, R. & Spracklen, D.V. 2007. Carbon mitigation by biofuels or by saving and restoring forests? *Science*, 317: 902.

Runge, C.F. & Senauer, B. 2007. How biofuels could starve the poor. *Foreign Affairs*, 86(3): 41–53.

Rutz, D. & Janssen, R. 2007. *Biofuel technology handbook*. Munich, Germany, WIP Renewable Energies.

Searchinger, T. 2008. *The impacts of biofuels on greenhouse gases: how land use change alters the equation*. Policy Brief. Washington, DC, The German Marshall Fund of the United States.

Searchinger, T., Heimlich, R., Houghton, R.A., Dong, F., Elobeid, A., Fabiosa, J., Tokgoz, S., Hayes, D. & Yu, T. 2008. Use of U.S. croplands for biofuels increases greenhouse gases through emissions from land use change. *Sciencexpress*, 7 February.

Senauer, B. & Sur, M. 2001. Ending global hunger in the 21st century: projections of the number of food insecure people. *Review of Agricultural Economics*, 23(1): 68–81.

Sexton, S., Rajagopal, D., Zilberman, D. & Roland-Holst, D. 2007. The intersections of energy and agriculture: implications of rising demand for biofuels and the search for the next generation. *ARE Update*, 10(5): 4–7.

Sharma, R. 2002. *The transmission of world price signals: concepts, issues and some evidence from Asian cereal markets*. Paper presented at the OECD Global Forum on Agriculture, May 2002, Rome.

Soyka, T., Palmer, C. & Engel, S. 2007. *The impacts of tropical biofuel production on land-use: the case of Indonesia*. Paper prepared for Tropentag 2007 Conference on International Agricultural Research and Development, 9–11 October 2007, University of Kassel, Witzenhausen and University of Göttingen, Germany.

Squizato, R. 2008. New approaches could increase biofuel output. *Bioenergy Business*, 2(2): 17 March.

Steenblik, R. 2007. *Biofuels – at what cost? Government support for ethanol and biodiesel in selected OECD countries*. Geneva, Switzerland, Global Subsidies Initiative, International Institute for Sustainable Development.

Strasberg, P.J., Jayne, T.S., Yamano, T., Nyoro, J., Karanja, D. & Strauss, J. 1999. *Effects of agricultural commercialization on food crop input use and productivity in Kenya*. MSU International Development Working Paper No. 71. East Lansing, MI, USA, Michigan State University.

Tefft, J. Forthcoming. White gold: cotton in francophone West Africa. *In* S. Haggblade & P. Hazell, eds. *Successes in African agriculture: lessons for the future*. Washington, DC, International Food Policy Research Institute.

The Royal Society. 2008. *Sustainable biofuels: prospects and challenges*. Policy document 01/08, January 2008. London.

Tiffany, D.G. & Eidman, V.R. 2003. *Factors associated with success of fuel ethanol producers*. Staff Paper Series P03-07. St. Paul, MN, USA, Department of Applied Economics, College of Agricultural, Food, and Environmental Sciences, University of Minnesota.

Tilman, D., Hill, J. & Lehman, C. 2006. Carbon-negative biofuels from low-input high-diversity grassland biomass. *Science,* 314(5805): 1598–1600.

Timmer, C.P. 1988. The agricultural transformation. *In* H. Chenergy & T.N. Srinivasan, eds. *Handbook of development economics,* Vol. I. Amsterdam, Elsevier Science Publishers.

Timmer, C.P. 2002. Agriculture and economic development. *In* B.L. Gardner & G.C. Rausser, eds. *Handbook of agricultural economics,* Vol. 2A. Amsterdam, North-Holland.

Tollefson, J. 2008. Not your father's biofuels. *Nature,* 451(21): 880–883.

Tyner, W.E. & Taheripour, F. 2007. *Biofuels, energy security, and global warming policy interactions.* Paper presented at the National Agricultural Biotechnology Council Conference, 22–24 May 2007, South Dakota State University, Brookings, SD, USA.

UNCTAD (United Nations Conference on Trade and Development). 2008. *Making certification work for sustainable development: the case of biofuels.* New York and Geneva, United Nations.

UNDP (United Nations Development Programme). 2004. *Reducing rural poverty through increased access to energy services: a review of the Multifunctional Platform Project in Mali.* Bamako.

UNICEF (United Nations Children's Fund). 2007. *The State of the World's Children 2007: women and children – the double dividend of gender equality.* New York, USA.

USDA (United States Department of Agriculture). 2008a. *Agricultural Baseline Projections: U.S. Crops, 2008-2017.* Web site (available at www.ers.usda.gov/Briefing/Baseline/crops.htm).

USDA. 2008b. *World Agricultural Supply and Demand Estimates: WASDE-459.* Released 10 June. Washington, DC.

USDA Foreign Agricultural Service. 2008. Production, supply and distribution online. Online database (available at www.fas.usda.gov/psdonline/psdhome.aspx).

von Braun, J. 1994. Production, employment, and income effects of commercialization of agriculture. *In* J. von Braun & E. Kennedy, eds. *Agricultural commercialization, economic development, and nutrition.* Baltimore, MD, USA, The Johns Hopkins University Press.

von Braun, J. & Kennedy, E. eds. 1994. *Agricultural commercialization, economic development, and nutrition.* Baltimore, MD, USA, The Johns Hopkins University Press.

Wilhelm, W.W., Johnson, J., Karlen, D. & Lightle, D. 2007. Corn stover to sustain organic carbon further constrains biomass supply. *Agronomy Journal,* 99: 1665-1667.

Westcott, P. 2007. *Ethanol expansion in the United States: how will the agricultural sector adjust?* FDS-07D-01. Washington, DC, Economic Research Service, United States Department of Agriculture.

World Bank. 2007. *World Development Report 2008.* Washington, DC.

WFP (World Food Programme). 2008. INTERFAIS. Online database (available at www.wfp.org/interfais/index2.htm).

Worldwatch Institute. 2006. *Biofuels for transportation: global potential and implications for sustainable agriculture and energy in the 21st century.* Washington, DC.

Yu, S. & Tao, J. 2008. Life cycle simulation-based economic and risk assessment of biomass-based fuel ethanol (BFE) projects in different feedstock planting areas. *Energy,* 33(2008): 375–384.

Zah, R., Böni, H., Gauch, M., Hischier, R., Lehmann, M. & Wäger, P. 2007. *Ökobilanz von Energieprodukten: Ökologische Bewertung von Biotreibstoffen.* St Gallen, Switzerland, Empa.

Special chapters of
The State of Food and Agriculture

In addition to the usual review of the recent world food and agricultural situation, each issue of this report since 1957 has included one or more special studies on problems of longer-term interest. Special chapters in earlier issues have covered the following subjects:

1957   Factors influencing the trend of food consumption
            Postwar changes in some institutional factors affecting agriculture
1958   Food and agricultural developments in Africa south of the Sahara
            The growth of forest industries and their impact on the world's forests
1959   Agricultural incomes and levels of living in countries at different stages of
            economic development
            Some general problems of agricultural development in less-developed
            countries in the light of postwar experience
1960   Programming for agricultural development
1961   Land reform and institutional change
            Agricultural extension, education and research in Africa, Asia
            and Latin America
1962   The role of forest industries in the attack on economic underdevelopment
            The livestock industry in less-developed countries
1963   Basic factors affecting the growth of productivity in agriculture
            Fertilizer use: spearhead of agricultural development
1964   Protein nutrition: needs and prospects
            Synthetics and their effects on agricultural trade
1966   Agriculture and industrialization
            Rice in the world food economy
1967   Incentives and disincentives for farmers in developing countries
            The management of fishery resources
1968   Raising agricultural productivity in developing countries through
            technological improvement
            Improved storage and its contribution to world food supplies
1969   Agricultural marketing improvement programmes:
            some lessons from recent experience
            Modernizing institutions to promote forestry development
1970   Agriculture at the threshold of the Second Development Decade
1971   Water pollution and its effects on living aquatic resources and fisheries
1972   Education and training for development
            Accelerating agricultural research in the developing countries
1973   Agricultural employment in developing countries
1974   Population, food supply and agricultural development
1975   The Second United Nations Development Decade:
            mid-term review and appraisal
1976   Energy and agriculture
1977   The state of natural resources and the human environment for food
            and agriculture
1978   Problems and strategies in developing regions
1979   Forestry and rural development
1980   Marine fisheries in the new era of national jurisdiction
1981   Rural poverty in developing countries and means of poverty alleviation
1982   Livestock production: a world perspective
1983   Women in developing agriculture
1984   Urbanization, agriculture and food systems

128